Practice and Homework Book

AUTHORS

PEGGY MORROW AND ANNE BOYD

An imprint of Addison Wesley Longman Ltd.

Don Mills, Ontario • Reading, Massachusetts
Harlow, England • Glenview, Illinois
Melbourne, Australia

GRADE 6

Consulting Editor: Lesley Haynes
Editors: Fran Cohen, Brenda McLoughlin, First Folio Resource Group Inc.
Design, Art Direction, and Page Composition: Brian Lehen • Graphic Design Ltd.
Illustrators: Sami Suomalainen, Brian Lehen

REVIEWERS:

Elaine Benton, Parent
North York
Ontario

Debbie Duvall
Mathematics Consultant
Elk Island Public Schools
Sherwood Park
Alberta

Shirley Fairfield
Independent Consultant
North York
Ontario

Sue Gordon
William Tredway Junior Public School
Toronto District School Board
Ontario

Michelle Jackson
Mathematics Consultant
Toronto Catholic District School Board
Ontario

Maria McMillan
Teacher
Upper Stewiate
Nova Scotia

This book contains recycled product and is acid free.
Printed and bound in Canada.

ISBN 0–201–43886–0

B C D E F – WC – 04 03 02 01 00 99

CONTENTS

Practice and Homework Pages

Computation Skills Bank

To the Teacher

This *Practice and Homework Book* provides reinforcement of the concepts and skills explored in the *Quest 2000 Exploring Mathematics* program.

There are two sections in the book. The first section follows the sequence of *Quest 2000 Exploring Mathematics*. It is intended for use throughout the year as you are teaching the program's eleven units and the Core Activities described in the *Teacher's Guide & Journal.* A two-page spread supports the content of each Core Activity within the units.

The two-page spread is linked to a unit activity.

The title identifies the learning outcome of the activity.

The left page is the "practice" page and is intended for classroom use following completion of the Core Activity.

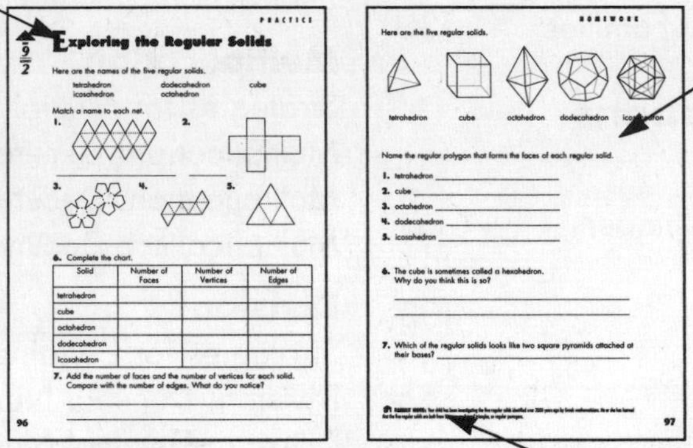

The right page is the "homework" page, to be completed by the child with the assistance of a family member.

The Family Note provides a simple explanation of the math the child is learning, as well as suggestions for helping the child.

The second section of the book is a *Computation Skills Bank* — a series of pages that you can use at any time to develop and maintain students' facility with basic facts and proficiency with computational strategies and skills. These pages provide ongoing practice and can be used in class or assigned as homework. The strategies pages help students use thinking strategies to derive the answers to the facts. Additional practice pages, which can be used as either class work or homework, can be found in the *Extra Practice and Testing Masters* component of the *Quest 2000 Exploring Mathematics* program.

To the Family

The homework pages in this book will help your child practise the mathematical skills and concepts that he or she is exploring at school. As you assist your child to complete each page, you will have an opportunity to become involved in your child's learning.

The homework page is always on the right page of a two-page spread and is closely linked to the content of the left page, which your child will have completed in class.

A Family Note at the bottom of each homework page explains the math your child is learning, and suggests some of the ways you can assist your child. Here are more ways to help:

- Read the instructions on the page with or for your child to make sure she or he understands what to do.
- Encourage your child to explain his or her thinking during the completion of the page.
- Some of the pages require mathematical tools. It would be helpful to have a ruler marked in centimetres and millimetres, a protractor, and a calculator.

These homework pages are intended to be enjoyable for you and your child, as well as to help your child improve his or her mathematical skills. Perhaps as you work through the book together, you will have other ideas for math activities that your child can share with the rest of the class.

This math workbook will be sent home frequently throughout the year. Please help your child complete the assigned page. Make sure the book is returned promptly, since it is to be used at school as well as at home.

To the Student

This book is designed to help you learn more about the mathematics topics you are studying in school. For each topic, you will find two practice pages — one to complete at school and one to complete at home with your family and friends.

Many students find that they have more success with homework if they develop regular routines. Here are some suggestions:

- Choose a quiet place where you can work without being disturbed.
- Work where you have enough space for your books and papers.
- Gather any equipment you need, such as pencils, erasers, a ruler, and a calculator.
- Check to make sure you have enough light and that your chair and your desk or table are the right height for working comfortably.

Try to find the study environment that works best for you. Use these questions to help you establish your own effective routine:

- When is the best time for completing homework — after school, after dinner?
- Do you work better if you have a healthy snack nearby?
- Do you understand some topics better if you discuss them with a classmate or an adult family member?
- How can you schedule your work to ensure that it all gets done without any last-minute panic?
- How often do you need to look back at the work you completed in the past, in order to make sure that you remember it?

We hope that you will enjoy using this book and that it will help you as you learn about math.

Practice and Homework Pages

Extending Growth Patterns

For each pattern, draw the next two figures and complete the T-table. Write a rule that relates the figure number to the total number of squares, circles, or small triangles.

1.

Figure 1 Figure 2 Figure 3 Figure 4 Figure 5

Rule: +2

Figure Number	Total Number of Squares
1	1
2	3
3	4
4	5
5	6

2.

Figure 1 Figure 2 Figure 3 Figure 4 Figure 5

Rule: x2

Figure Number	Total Number of Circles
1	1
2	6
3	12
4	24
5	36

3.

Figure 1 Figure 2 Figure 3 Figure 4

Rule: +3

Figure Number	Total Number of Small Triangles
1	1
2	3
3	6
4	9

Draw the next figure in each group.
Complete each T-table, extending it to the tenth figure.
Write the rule that relates the figure number to the total number of squares.

1.

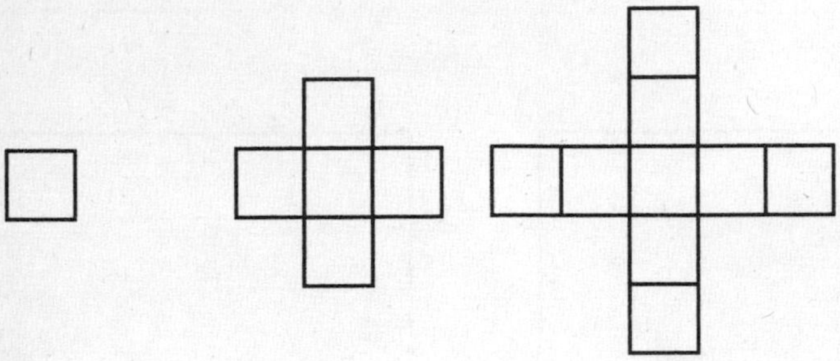

Figure Number	Total Number of Squares
1	1
2	4
3	8
4	16
5	20
6	24
7	28
8	32
9	36
10	40

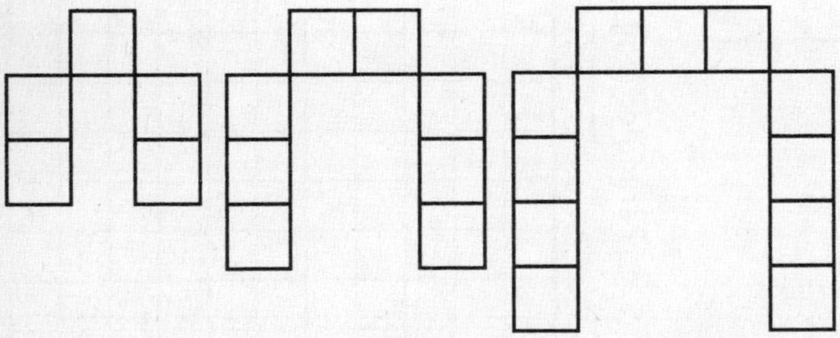

Figure 1 Figure 2 Figure 3 Figure 4

Rule: +4 ______________________

____

2.

Figure Number	Total Number of Squares
1	5
2	8
3	11
4	14
5	17
6	20
7	23
8	26
9	29
10	32

Figure 1 Figure 2 Figure 3 Figure 4

Rule: +3 ______________________

____

FAMILY NOTE: Your child is exploring growth patterns. Ask him or her to explain how each figure in the pattern is different from the preceding figure. Your child should be able to find a numeric relationship between the figure number and the corresponding number of squares, and use this relationship to extend each T-table.

Graphing Ordered Pairs

Find the side length and perimeter of each square.
Record the data in the T-table.
Write ordered pairs.

Graph the points on the coordinate grid and connect the points.

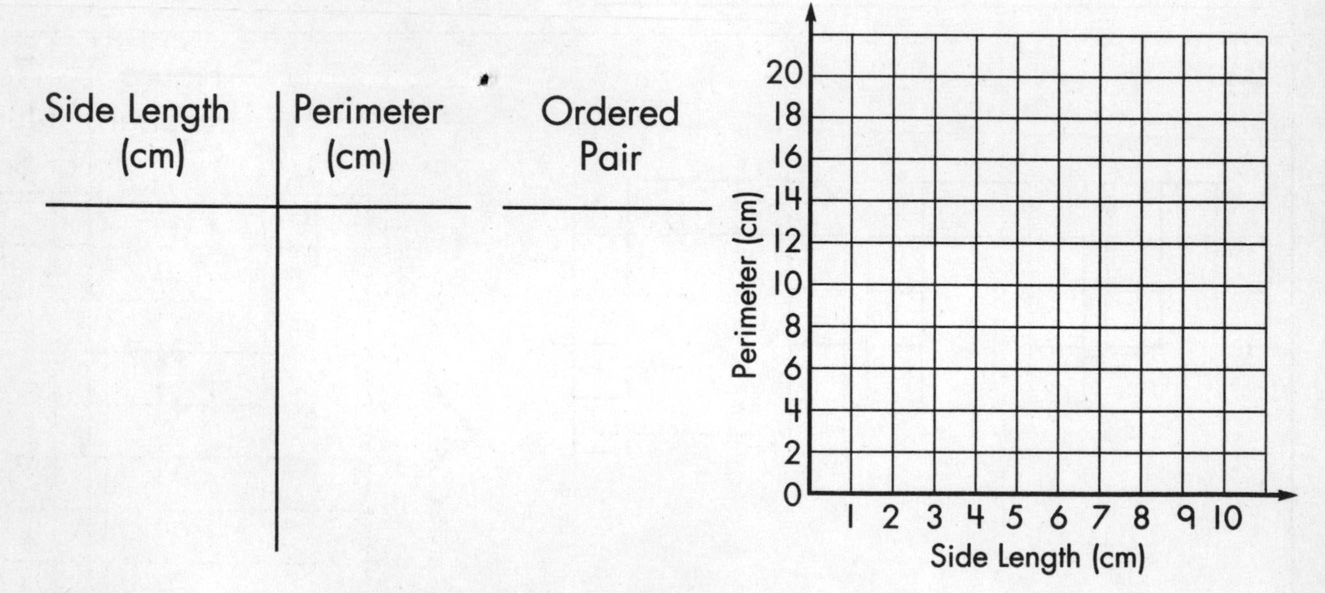

Write the rule for finding the perimeter of a square when you know the side length.

____

____

Write a list of ordered pairs for each T-table.
Plot the ordered pairs and connect the points.
Write a rule that relates the first number to the second number.

1.

First Number	Second Number	Ordered Pair
1	5	______
2	8	______
3	11	______
4	14	______

Rule: ______________________________

____

Second Number: 0 2 4 6 8 10 12 14 16
First Number: 1 2 3 4 5 6 7 8

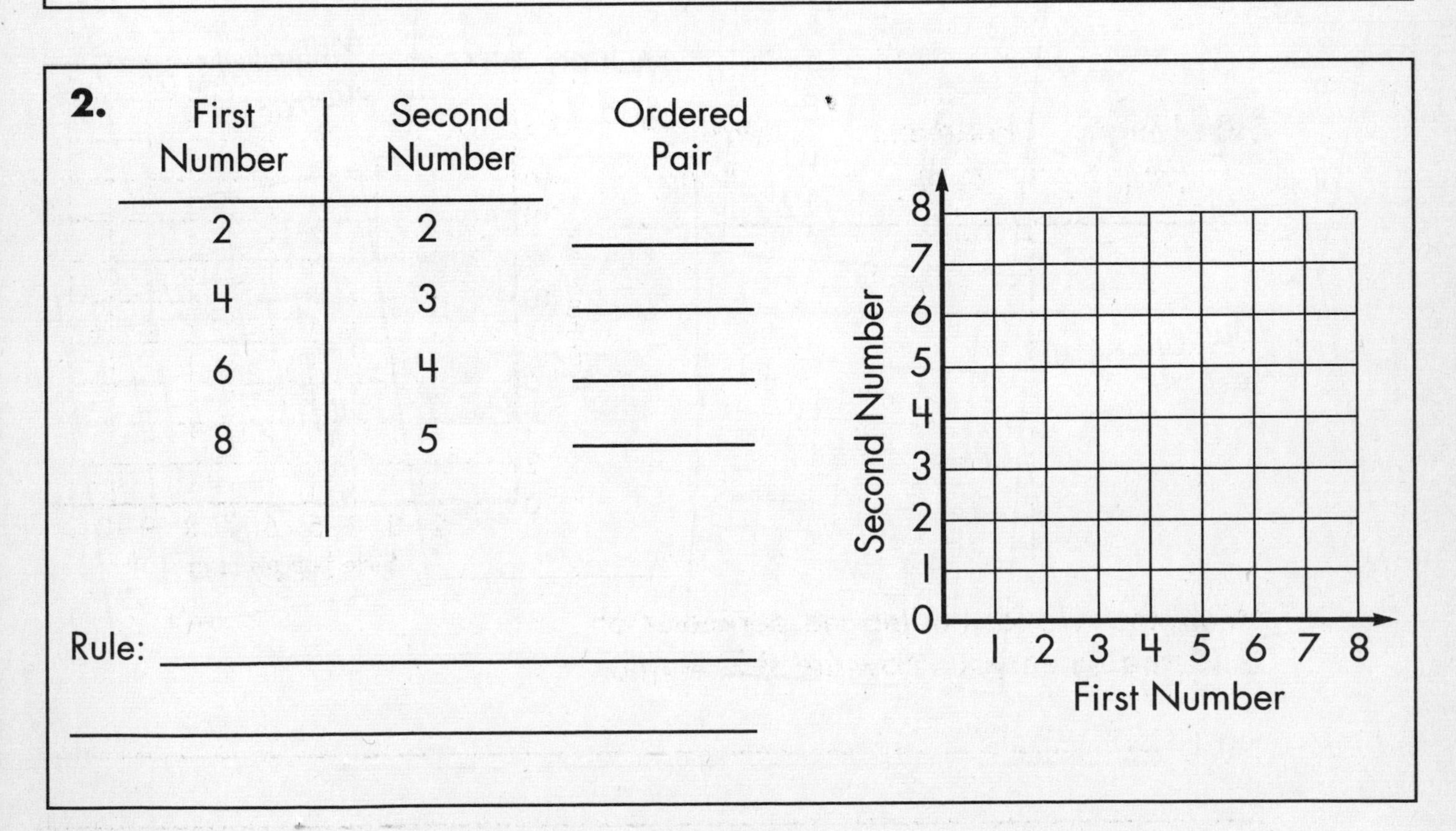

2.

First Number	Second Number	Ordered Pair
2	2	______
4	3	______
6	4	______
8	5	______

Rule: ______________________________

____

FAMILY NOTE: Your child is learning to show relationships between sets of data by generating ordered pairs and plotting them on a coordinate grid. Ask your child to explain how he or she graphed the ordered pairs.

Matching Representations

Find three matching sets.
Write the letters for each set.
Each set must have a pattern, a T-table, a graph, and a rule.

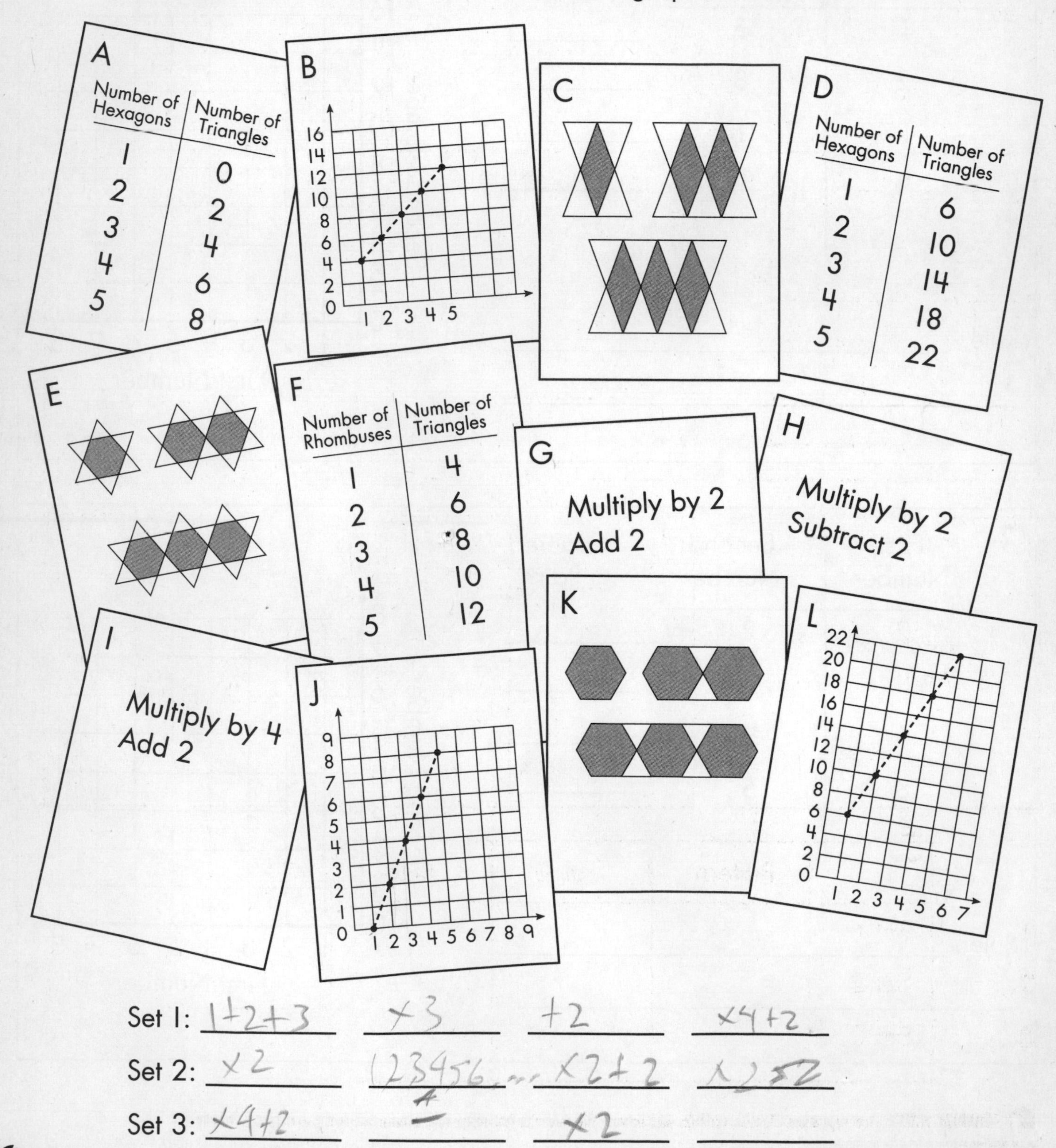

Set 1: 1+2+3 ×3 +2 ×4+2

Set 2: ×2 123456... ×2+2 ×2−2

Set 3: ×4+2 4 — ×2

Find three matching sets.
Each set must have a pattern, a T-table, and a rule.

A

Number of Trapezoids	Number of Triangles
1	2
2	3
3	4
4	5
5	6

B

Multiply by 3

C

Figure Number	Number of Sticks
1	3
2	5
3	7
4	9
5	11

D

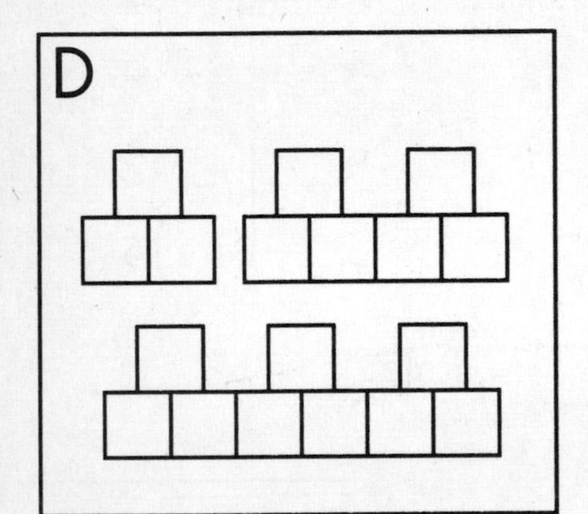

E

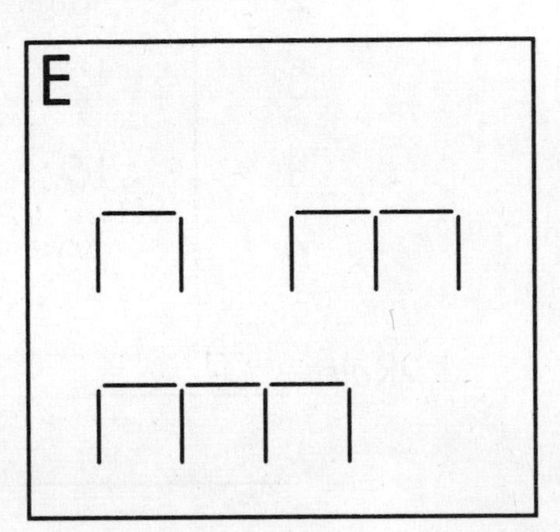

F

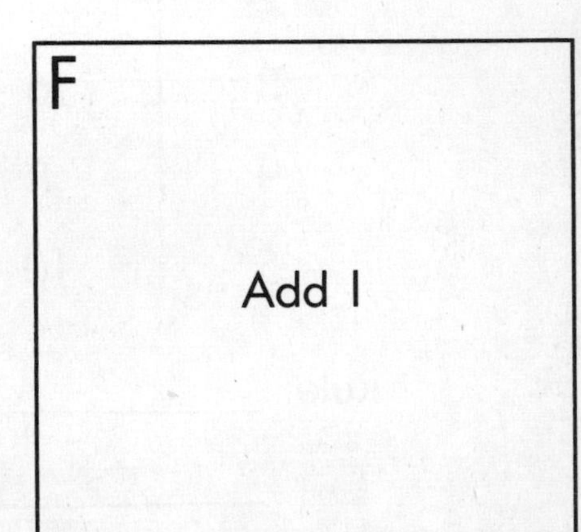

Add 1

G

Multiply by 2
Add 1

H

Figure Number	Number of Squares
1	3
2	6
3	9
4	12
5	15

I

		Pattern	T-table	Rule
1.	Set 1			
2.	Set 2			
3.	Set 3			

FAMILY NOTE: Matching patterns, T-tables, and rules will help your child recognize that relationships between two quantities can be represented in several ways.

Graphing Rules

Write a rule for each T-table.
Graph each rule on the coordinate grid.

1.

First Number	Second Number
1	2
2	4
3	6
4	8
5	10

Rule: x2 ______

2.

First Number	Second Number
1	4
2	8
3	12
4	16
5	20

Rule: x4 ______

3.

First Number	Second Number
1	3
2	6
3	9
4	12
5	15

Rule: x3 ______

4.

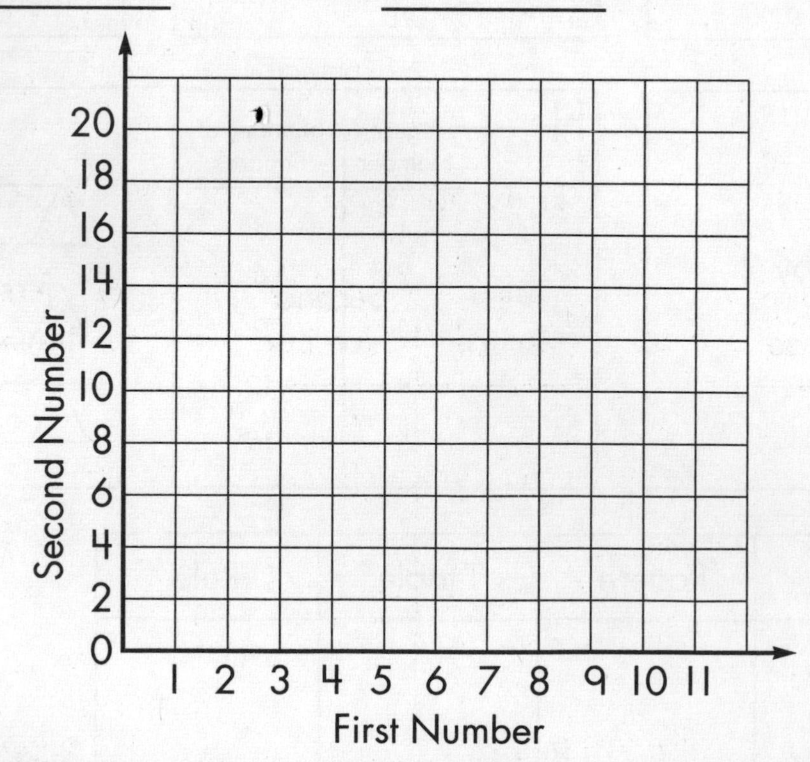

5. What patterns do you see in the graph? They are all numbers

Make a T-table for each set of points on the coordinate grid.
Write a rule for each T-table.

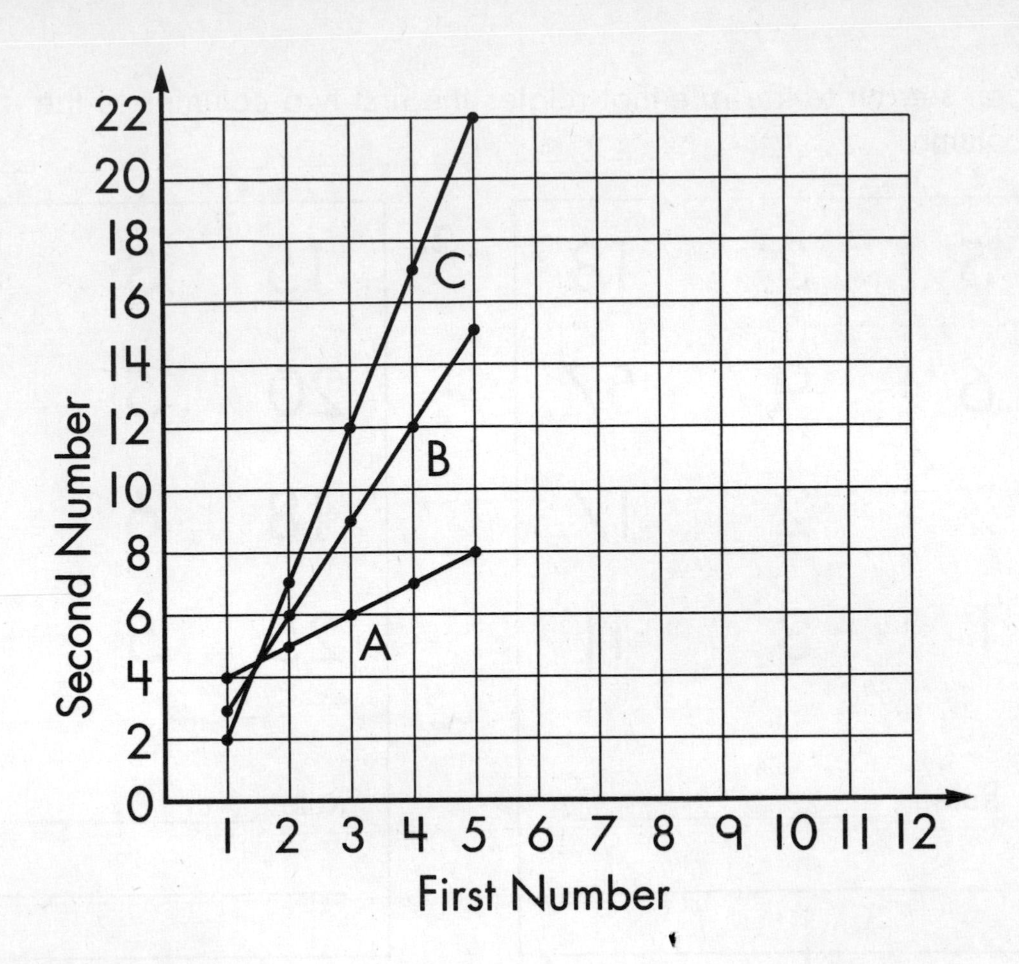

1. Graph A

First Number	Second Number
1	4
2	5
3	6
4	7
5	8

Rule: +3 ______________

____

2. Graph B

First Number	Second Number
1	3
2	6
3	9
4	12
5	15

Rule: x3 ______________

____

3. Graph C

First Number	Second Number
1	2
2	7
3	12
4	17
5	22

Rule: +5-3 ______________

____

FAMILY NOTE: Ask your child to explain why Graph B is steeper than Graph A, and Graph C is steeper than Graph B.

Relating Three Numbers

For each set, write the rule that relates the first two columns to the third column.

1.

5	3	18
6	9	57
7	2	17
1	8	11

Rule: ______________________

____

2.

15	3	6
20	5	5
18	6	4
25	5	6

Rule: ______________________

____

3.

18	8	14
24	6	22
19	7	16
16	9	11

Rule: ______________________

____

4.

3	9	25
2	20	38
9	8	70
7	6	40

Rule: ______________________

____

For each set, write the rule that relates the first two columns to the third. Write another set of numbers that follows the rule.

1.

9	8	14
10	10	17
15	8	20
12	16	25
___	___	___

Rule: ______________

____

2.

49	7	7
60	10	6
72	8	9
35	7	5
___	___	___

Rule: ______________

____

3.

5	8	26
9	7	32
8	9	34
16	15	62
___	___	___

Rule: ______________

____

4.

42	6	11
18	2	13
24	6	8
15	3	9
___	___	___

Rule: ______________

____

FAMILY NOTE: The work on this page extends your child's understanding of functional relationships. Ask your child to explain the rule for each set of numbers.

Understanding Large Numbers

Billions			Millions			Thousands			Units		
Hundreds	Tens	Ones	Hundreds	Tens	Ones	Hundreds	Tens	Ones	Hundreds	Tens	Ones

Write the digits in each period named.

1. 83 507 426
thousands 7

2. 1 286 153 419
billions 1

3. 5 576 342
millions 5

4. 73 165 247
millions 3

5. 6 814 377
units 7

6. 2 736 452
thousands 6

7. 2 906 325
millions 2

8. 75 861 000
thousands 1

9. 3 489 620
units 0

Write the value of each underlined digit.

10. 186 279 508 6 million

11. 2 376 543 215 6 million

12. 9 204 671 327 9 billion

13. 891 472 694 90 million

14. 506 333 295 300 thousand

15. 4 976 312 855 4 billion

Use the number in the box.
Write the digit in the place named.

81 764 237

1. hundreds ______

2. millions ______

3. ten thousands ______

4. ones ______

5. ten millions ______

6. thousands ______

7. tens ______

8. hundred thousands ______

2 706 842 603

9. hundred thousands ______

10. thousands ______

11. hundreds ______

12. tens ______

13. ones ______

14. millions ______

15. ten thousands ______

16. billions ______

17. hundred millions ______

18. ten millions ______

FAMILY NOTE: Working with very large numbers helps to refine your child's understanding of our base 10 number system. Refer your child to the place value chart at the top of the previous page to help in completing this page.

UNIT 2 ACTIVITY 2

Representing Numbers

Write each number in standard form.

1. 4.6 million ______
2. 1.7 billion ______
3. 1.5 million ______
4. 7.3 billion ______
5. 1.4 million ______

Write each number in words.

6. 3 647 227 ______
7. 2 361 576 212 ______
8. 25 636 208 ______
9. 45 396 ______

Write a rounded number for each.

10. 537 624 500 000

11. 1 967 485 132 ______

12. 25 962 378 ______

13. 1 131 867 ______

14. 47 285 152 ______

15. 999 478 ______

Write a rounded number for each.

1. 502 387 500 000 ________ **2.** 5896 ________

3. 1 002 974 ________ **4.** 2 002 974 ________

5. 44 692 ________ **6.** 897 462 005 ________

7. 998 917 ________ **8.** 1 002 453 ________

9. 29 571 161 ________ **10.** 1 932 465 819 ________

Round each decimal number to the nearest whole number.

11. 2.088 ________ **12.** 9.9716 ________

13. 36.690 ________ **14.** 13.7815 ________

15. 1828.423 ________ **16.** 599.054 ________

17. 0.7823 ________ **18.** 74.08 ________

19. 285.099 ________ **20.** 6.973 ________

Round each amount.

21. $3297.53 $3000 ________

22. $298.43 ________

23. $15.3 billion ________

24. $1 232 642.45 ________

25. $7.9 million ________

26. $16.09 ________

27. $999 million ________

FAMILY NOTE: Your child is learning that numbers can be represented in many ways, and that numbers in newspaper headlines are often rounded. Help your child find examples of newspaper headlines containing numbers. Discuss whether the numbers are exact or rounded.

Exploring Powers of 10

Complete each chart to show what happens when you multiply by powers of 10.

1.

Millions			Thousands			Units			
Hundreds	Tens	Ones	Hundreds	Tens	Ones	Hundreds	Tens	Ones	
							7	0	7 × 10
						7	0	0	7 × 100
					7	0	0	0	7 × 1000
				7	6	0	0	0	7 × 10 000
			7	0	0	0	0	0	7 × 100 000
		7	0	0	0	0	0	0	7 × 1 000 000

2.

Millions			Thousands			Units			
Hundreds	Tens	Ones	Hundreds	Tens	Ones	Hundreds	Tens	Ones	
						6	8	0	68 × 10
					6	8	0	0	68 × 100
				6	8	0	0	0	68 × 1000
			6	8	0	0	0	0	68 × 10 000
		6	8	0	0	0	0	0	68 × 100 000
	6	8	0	0	0	0	0	0	68 × 1 000 000

3. Write about the patterns you see in your charts.

add a zero to every part.

Write each expression as a power of 10.
Then write it in standard form.

	Expanded Form	Power of 10	Standard Form
1.	10 × 10	10^2	100
2.	10 × 10 × 10	10^3	200
3.	10 × 10 × 10 × 10	10^4	300
4.	10 × 10 × 10 × 10 × 10	10^5	400
5.	10 × 10 × 10 × 10 × 10 × 10	10^6	600
6.	10 × 10 × 10 × 10 × 10 × 10 × 10	10^7	700

Write each power of 10 in expanded form.

7. 10^3 10 × 10 × 10

8. 10^7 10 × 10 × 10 × 10 × 10 × 10 × 10 ×

9. 10^6 10 × 10 × 10 × 10 × 10 × 10

10. 10^9 10 × 10 × 10 × 10 × 10 × 10 × 10 × 10 × 10

11. 10^8 10 × 10 × 10 × 10 × 10 × 10 × 10 × 10

12. 10^4 10 × 10 × 10 × 10

Write each power of 10 in standard form.

13. 10^5 50

14. 10^3 30

15. 10^1 10

16. 10^4 40

FAMILY NOTE: Your child is using powers of 10 to analyze the patterns that occur as place values increase and decrease. If possible, please provide a calculator for your child to use as he or she completes this page.

Understanding Small Numbers

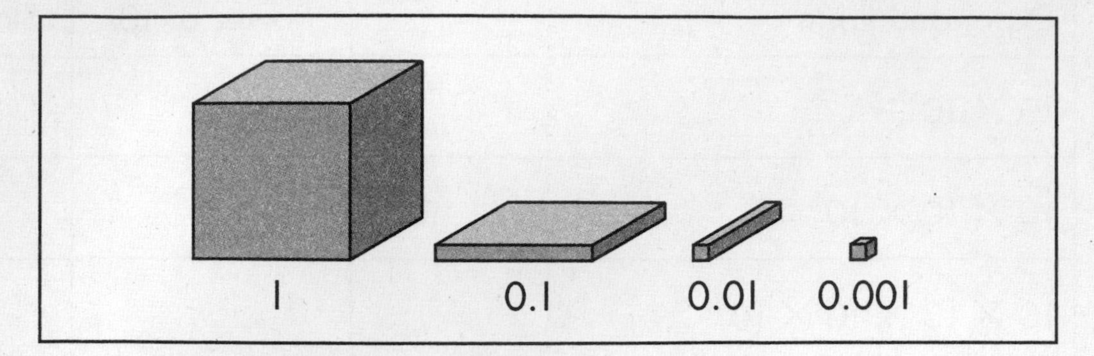

Write the decimal number represented by the blocks.

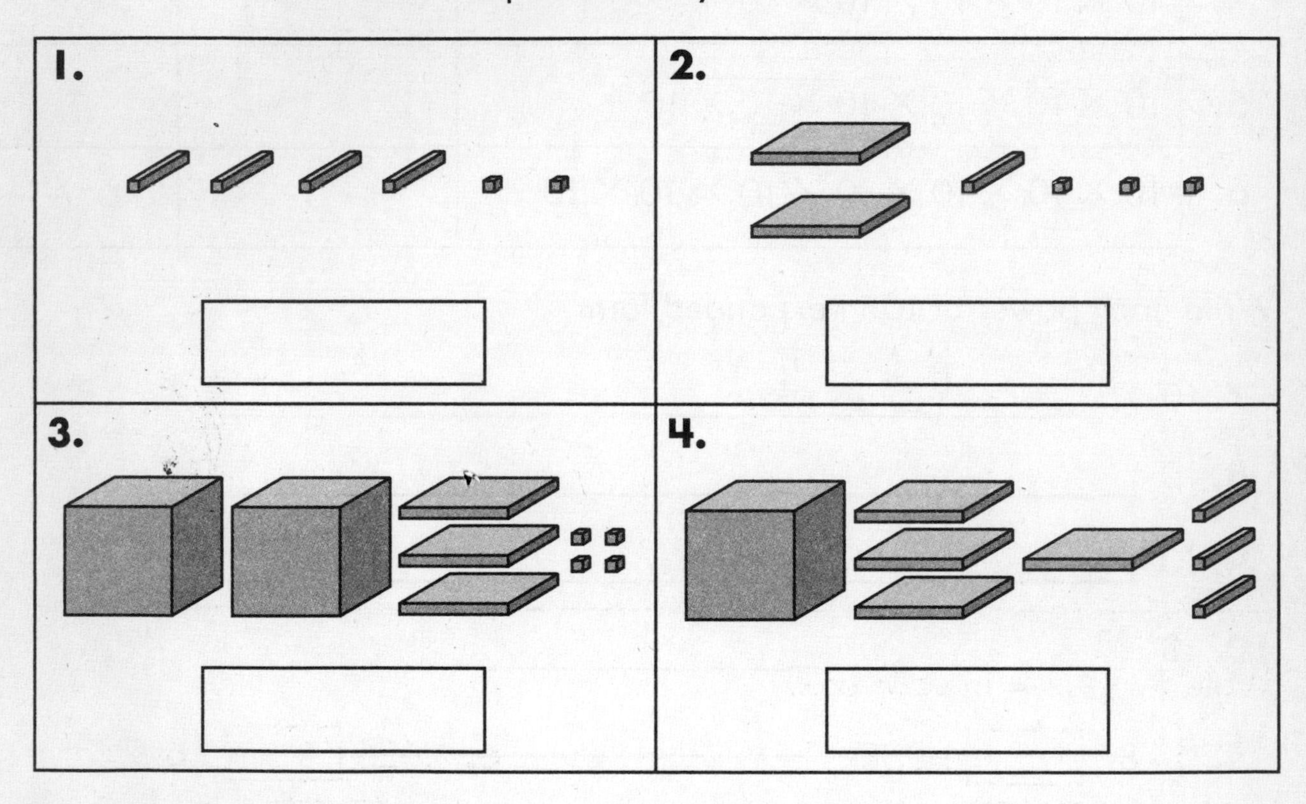

List each set of numbers from least to greatest.

5. 0.485, 1.267, 0.493 ____________________

6. 0.326, 0.301, 0.304 ____________________

7. 2.765, 2.932, 2.250 ____________________

8. 0.52, 0.43, 0.410 ____________________

9. 5.23, 5.15, 5.67 ____________________

10. 8.623, 8.251, 82.716 ____________________

Draw base 10 blocks to represent each number.

1. 2.672	**2.** 0.943
3. 0.057	**4.** 1.483

Write >, <, or = in each box.

5. 0.789 ☐ 1.358

6. 1.625 ☐ 1.607

7. 0.227 ☐ 0.225

8. 3.8 ☐ 3.800

9. 3.250 ☐ 4.976

10. 1.731 ☐ 1.645

11. 0.23 ☐ 0.230

12. 11.07 ☐ 11.16

13. 24.076 ☐ 4.958

14. 0.111 ☐ 0.213

15. 0.132 ☐ 0.137

16. 5.137 ☐ 5.048

FAMILY NOTE: Your child is learning to read, write, and interpret decimal numbers. The illustration at the top of the previous page will help your child complete Problems 1 to 4 on this page.

Using Decimal Numbers to Measure Length

Estimate each length in millimetres.
Convert each estimate to centimetres and metres.
Then measure and record the actual length in millimetres.
Convert the actual measurement to centimetres and metres as well.

What to Measure	Estimate	Actual Measurement
1. width of your math book	______ mm ______ cm ______ m	______ mm ______ cm ______ m
2. length of your math book	______ mm ______ cm ______ m	______ mm ______ cm ______ m
3. thickness of your math book	______ mm ______ cm ______ m	______ mm ______ cm ______ m
4. length of a friend's hair	______ mm ______ cm ______ m	______ mm ______ cm ______ m
5. width of your thumb	______ mm ______ cm ______ m	______ mm ______ cm ______ m

Complete the table.

	Millimetres	Centimetres	Metres
1.	50	5	
2.	73		
3.		95	
4.			0.1
5.	180		
6.		35	
7.		68	
8.			0.75
9.	87		
10.			0.02
11.		100	

FAMILY NOTE: Your child is learning to use decimals to express metric measures of length. Ask your child to describe how to convert from a larger unit to a smaller one, and from a smaller unit to a larger one. Provide your child with a calculator, if one is available, to assist in the conversions.

Exploring Multiples

Write the first ten multiples of each number.

1. 3: ___ ___ ___ ___ ___ ___ ___ ___ ___ ___

2. 4: ___ ___ ___ ___ ___ ___ ___ ___ ___ ___

3. 7: ___ ___ ___ ___ ___ ___ ___ ___ ___ ___

4. 9: ___ ___ ___ ___ ___ ___ ___ ___ ___ ___

5. 11: ___ ___ ___ ___ ___ ___ ___ ___ ___ ___

6. Write the first ten multiples of 6 and the first ten multiples of 8. Circle all the common multiples of 6 and 8.

6: ___ ___ ___ ___ ___ ___ ___ ___ ___ ___

8: ___ ___ ___ ___ ___ ___ ___ ___ ___ ___

Write the first three common multiples of each pair of numbers. Circle the least common multiple.

7. 3 and 6 ________ ________ ________

8. 4 and 7 ________ ________ ________

9. 5 and 8 ________ ________ ________

10. 6 and 10 ________ ________ ________

Write the least common multiple of each pair of numbers.

11. 2 and 3 ________

12. 2 and 5 ________

13. 4 and 5 ________

14. 4 and 6 ________

1. Circle the multiples of 6.
Cross the multiples of 9.

1	2	3	4	5	6	7	8	9	10
11	12	13	14	15	16	17	18	19	20
21	22	23	24	25	26	27	28	29	30
31	32	33	34	35	36	37	38	39	40
41	42	43	44	45	46	47	48	49	50
51	52	53	54	55	56	57	58	59	60
61	62	63	64	65	66	67	68	69	70
71	72	73	74	75	76	77	78	79	80
81	82	83	84	85	86	87	88	89	90
91	92	93	94	95	96	97	98	99	100

2. List the common multiples of 6 and 9 up to 100.
Circle the least common multiple.

____

Write the least common multiple of each set of numbers.

3. 6 and 8 ____________

4. 8 and 10 ____________

5. 5 and 8 ____________

6. 3 and 5 ____________

7. 3, 4, and 5 ____________

8. 4, 6, and 8 ____________

FAMILY NOTE: To work with multiples, it is essential for your child to be proficient with skip counting by 2s, 3s, 4s … 12s. Encourage your child to practise skip counting frequently. You might play a game where you and your child take turns saying alternate numbers in a counting sequence.

Exploring Factors

List all the factors of each number.

1. 21 ____________________ **2.** 31 ____________________

3. 16 ____________________ **4.** 35 ____________________

5. 41 ____________________ **6.** 81 ____________________

7. 36 ____________________ **8.** 60 ____________________

____________________ ____________________

List the common factors of each pair of numbers.
Circle the greatest common factor.

9. 6 and 10 ____________ **10.** 12 and 20 ____________

11. 8 and 20 ____________ **12.** 30 and 32 ____________

13. 14 and 21 ____________ **14.** 18 and 30 ____________

15. List five prime numbers (numbers with only two factors).

______ ______ ______ ______ ______

16. List five composite numbers (numbers with three or more factors).

______ ______ ______ ______ ______

Write *prime* or *composite* for each number.

17. 27 ____________ **18.** 19 ____________

19. 17 ____________ **20.** 36 ____________

21. 43 ____________ **22.** 8 ____________

23. 61 ____________ **24.** 84 ____________

1. Record all the factors of each number in the table.
Tell how many factors each number has.

Number	Factors	Number of Factors
21		
22		
23		
24		
25		
26		
27		
28		
29		
30		

2. Write the prime numbers between 21 and 30.

____

3. Write all the prime numbers less than 50.

____

____

4. Which prime number is an even number? ________

FAMILY NOTE: Ask your child to explain how to find all the factors of a given number and how to determine whether a number is prime.

Solving Money Problems

Anna and Jacob went to a sports shop.
Each bought three different items from the list.
Anna spent about $150 and Jacob about $250.
Fill out an invoice for each person, showing the items bought and their cost.

Today's Specials
All prices include taxes

In-line skates	$87.95 per pair
Tennis racquets	$69.99 each
Golf clubs	$39.99 each
Baseballs	$19.75 each
Basketballs	$45.50 each
Jogging suits	$79.95 each

1. *Anna*

Item	Cost ($)
Total	$

2. *Jacob*

Item	Cost ($)
Total	$

3. How much change did Anna get from $150? $ ________

4. How much change did Jacob get from $300? $ ________

Estimate the total for each sales receipt.
Then find each actual total.

1. Estimate: $ ________

29.78
62.49
37.15
60.99
55.45

Total $ ____

2. Estimate: $ ________

17.77
81.35
2.95
40.32
25.11
16.88

Total $ ____

3. Estimate: $ ________

4.27
10.95
15.03
31.25
18.20

Total $ ____

4. Estimate: $ ________

36.19
29.95
7.11
18.99
12.02

Total $ ____

5. Estimate: $ ________

7.95
16.38
41.02
9.95
23.19

Total $ ____

6. Estimate: $ ________

8.25
15.19
6.95
32.50
14.62

Total $ ____

FAMILY NOTE: Estimating money amounts is a skill frequently used in everyday life. Ask your child to share her or his estimation strategies with you.

Using Strategies to Add and Subtract

Calculate each sum or difference. Use any procedure you wish.
Show all your work.
If you need help, turn to pages 131, 136, 152 and 156.

1. 4862 + 9378 = _______	**2.** 876 + 964 + 389 = _______
3. 68.23 + 97.86 = _______	**4.** 8600 – 7286 = _______
5. 11.01 – 0.673 = _______	**6.** 92.287 – 1.37 = _______

Calculate each sum or difference. Use any procedure you wish.
Show all your work.
Ask a family member to do Problems 1 and 5 on paper.
Then explain your procedures to one another.

1. 495 + 625 = _______	**2.** 93.26 + 85.14 = _______
3. 76 + 187 + 493 = _______	**4.** 9632 – 4968 = _______
5. 27.306 – 18.27 = _______	**6.** 6000 – 485 = _______

FAMILY NOTE: Exploring different ways to add and subtract can help your child develop a better understanding of these operations. Your child may use the standard procedure or a personal method that makes sense to him or her. Please share your procedures for adding and subtracting with your child and have your child compare his or her procedures with yours. Pages 131, 136, 152 and 156 in this book show several adding and subtracting strategies.

Using Multiplication and Division

Solve the problems. Write number sentences to show how you solved them.

1. The average person's hair grows 0.83 cm in a month. If you had never had a haircut, how long would your hair be now?

____

____

2. Suppose the average banana has a mass of about 200 g. About how many bananas would there be in a pile with the same mass as you?

____

____

3. A paper cup holds about 180 mL of liquid. About how many paper cups could you fill with a 2 L container of milk?

____

____

4. A dime has a mass of about 2 g. About how many dimes can you lift? Explain your thinking.

____

____

5. A car travels 37 km in one half hour. At this speed, how long would it take the car to travel 500 km?

____

____

Solve the problems. Write number sentences to show how you solved them.

1. Suppose you floss your teeth once a day, using about 30 cm of dental floss. How long would this package of dental floss last?

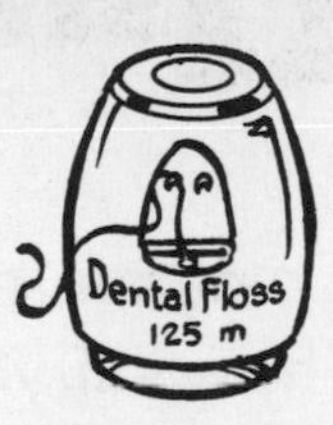

2. Suppose the average person uses 15 mL of mustard on a hot dog. About how many bottles this size would you need for 1000 hot dogs, if everyone uses mustard?

3. It takes about 25 mL of chocolate mix to make a milk shake. How many milk shakes could you make with this bottle of chocolate mix?

4. This laundry detergent is good for 34 loads of wash.

a) About how many grams are needed for one load of wash?

b) How many boxes would your family need in one year?

FAMILY NOTE: The work on this page gives your child practice with using multiplication and division to solve problems. Ask your child to explain his or her thinking as she or he chooses one or more operations to use.

Using Strategies to Multiply

Calculate each product. Use any procedure you wish.
Show all your work. If you need help, turn to pages 141 and 160.

1. 768 × 25 = ________	**2.** 906 × 73 = ________
3. 6.29 × 8 = ________	**4.** 27.4 × 6 = ________
5. 0.256 × 7 = ________	**6.** 2.358 × 5 = ________

Calculate each product. Use any procedure you wish.
Show all your work.
Ask a family member to do Problems 1 and 3 on paper.
Explain your procedures to one another.

1. $857 \times 38 =$ ________	**2.** $752 \times 69 =$ ________
3. $0.312 \times 9 =$ ________	**4.** $0.76 \times 24 =$ ________
5. $3.202 \times 8 =$ ________	**6.** $60.25 \times 7 =$ ________

FAMILY NOTE: To find the products, your child may wish to use the standard procedure or a personal method that makes sense to him or her. Please share your procedure for multiplying with your child and have your child compare his or her procedure with yours. Refer to pages 141 and 160 for several strategies that can be used to multiply.

Finding Unit Prices

Find the unit price for each item.
Round to the nearest cent if necessary.

Find the unit price for each quantity.
Round to the nearest cent if necessary.
Circle the better buy.

		Unit Price
1. Bird seed:	8 kg for $5.95	________
	20 kg for $13.95	________
2. Markers:	8 for $4.99	________
	12 for $7.80	________
3. Paper plates:	50 for $2.95	________
	100 for $3.50	________
4. Bananas:	3 kg for $1.89	________
	5 kg for $3.19	________
5. Apple juice:	2 L for $1.99	________
	4 L for $3.89	________
6. Plastic wrap:	90 m for $3.09	________
	70 m for $2.79	________
7. Oranges:	4 for $0.99	________
	6 for $1.59	________
8. Bleach:	2 L for $1.99	________
	5 L for $6.25	________

FAMILY NOTE: Your child has been using division to find unit prices. You can give your child additional practice with this skill using advertised grocery prices for different-sized packages or different brands.

Using Strategies to Divide

Calculate each quotient. Use any procedure you wish.
Show all your work.
If you need help, turn to pages 146 and 164.

1. 823 ÷ 6 = ________	**2.** 967 ÷ 23 = ________
3. 4806 ÷ 35 = ________	**4.** 2.75 ÷ 5 = ________
5. 0.973 ÷ 7 = ________	**6.** 2.538 ÷ 6 = ________

Calculate each quotient. Use any procedure you wish.
Show all your work.
Ask a family member to do Problems 1 and 4 on paper.
Explain your procedures to one another.

1. 968 ÷ 5 = ______	**2.** 674 ÷ 21 = ______
3. 9733 ÷ 14 = ______	**4.** 96.6 ÷ 7 = ______
5. 2.382 ÷ 6 = ______	**6.** 1.473 ÷ 3 = ______

FAMILY NOTE: To find the quotients, your child may wish to use the standard procedure or a personal method that makes sense to him or her. Please share your procedure for dividing with your child and have your child compare his or her procedure with yours. Refer to pages 146 and 164 for several strategies that can be used to divide.

Solving Number Logic Puzzles

Solve each puzzle.

1. I am a number. Divide me by 12. Multiply the quotient by 11. The result is 44. What number am I?	**2.** I am a number. Double me. Multiply by 7. The result is 84. What number am I?
3. I am a number. Subtract me from 80. Multiply the difference by 4. The result is 120. What number am I?	**4.** I am a number. Take one fourth of me. Multiply by 6. The result is 48. What number am I?
5. I am a number. Take one third of me. Add 30. The result is 66. What number am I?	**6.** I am a number. Subtract me from 45. Divide by 5. The result is 5. What number am I?

Solve each puzzle.

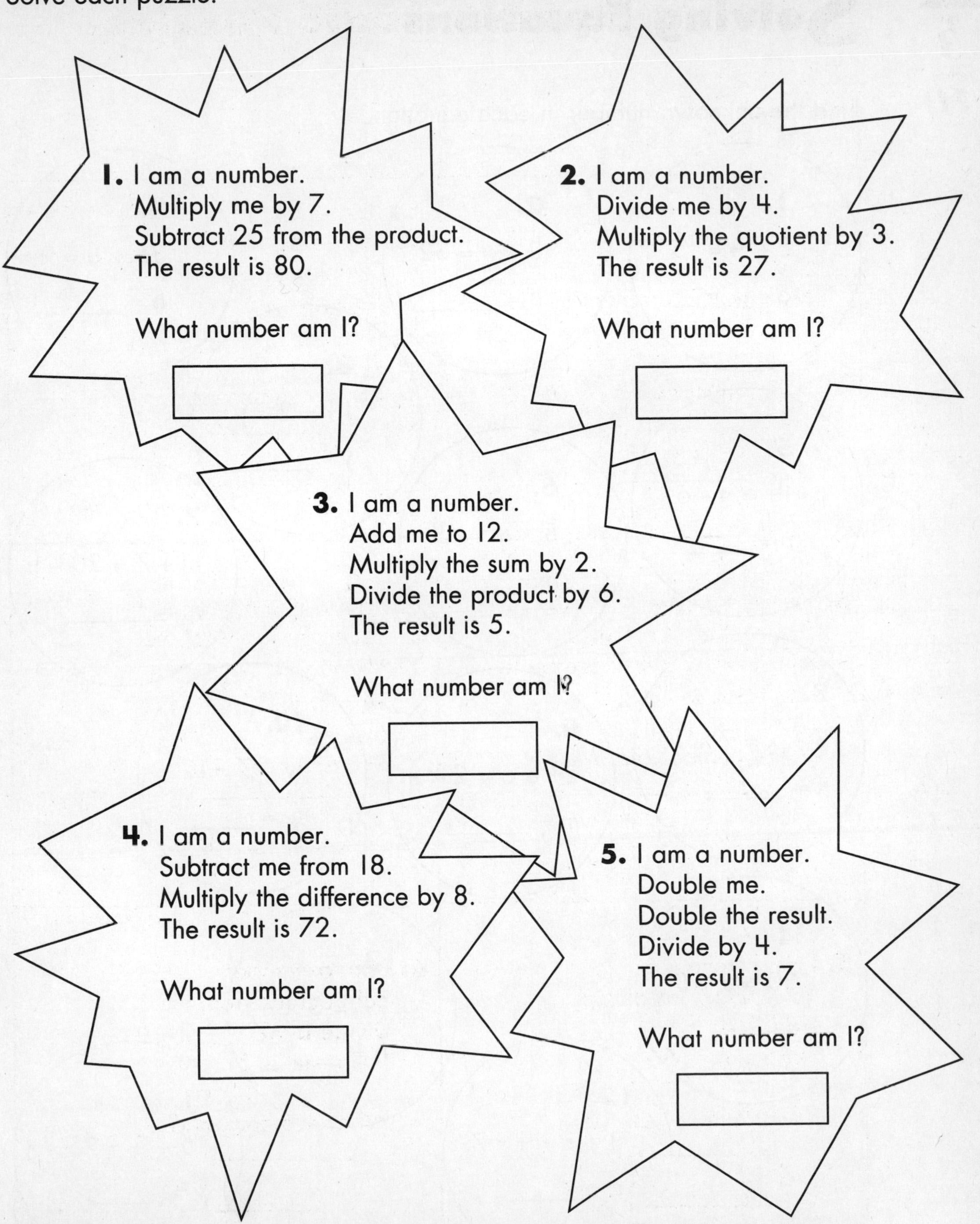

FAMILY NOTE: Your child has been using logical reasoning to solve number puzzles about an unknown value. This work helps to build a foundation for the study of algebra in later grades. Encourage your child to share the strategies he or she uses to solve the puzzles on this page.

Solving Equations

Find the unknown number in each equation.

1.
$c + 9 = 15$
$c =$ 6

2.
$8 \times n = 32$
$n =$ 4

3.
$14 = 2 \times y$
$y =$ 7

4.
$36 \div b = 9$
$b =$ 4

5.
$14 = n - 6$
$n =$ 8

6.
$8 \times m = 64$
$m =$ 8

7.
$m + 7 = 20 - 4$
$m =$ 9

8.
$8 + x = 7 + 10$
$x =$ 9

9.
$24 \div 6 = 2 \times m$
$m =$ 2

10.
$y - 7 = 12$
$y =$ 19

11.
$30 = s + 8$
$s =$ 22

12.
$3 + r = 4 \times 7$
$r =$ 25

13.
$27 = 3 \times n$
$n =$ 8

14.
$15 \div 3 = 25 \div y$
$y =$ 5

Find each unknown number.

1. $9 \times m = 72$

$m =$ 8

2. $n + 14 = 20$

$n =$ 6

3. $q \div 6 = 4$

$q =$ 2

4. $15 - n = 9$

$n =$ 6

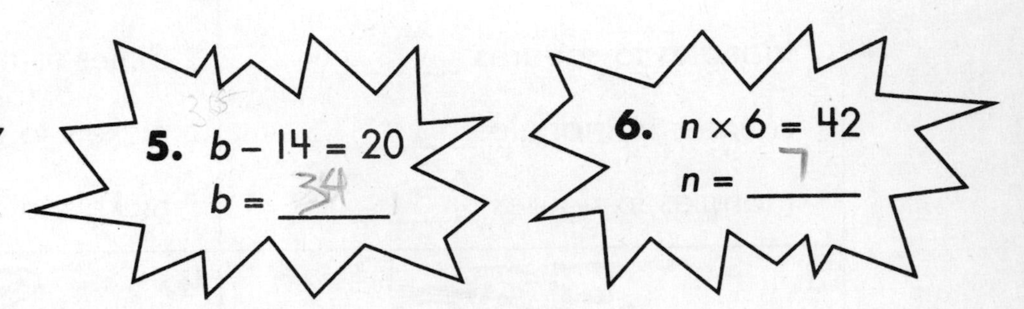

5. $b - 14 = 20$

$b =$ 34

6. $n \times 6 = 42$

$n =$ 7

7. $5 + n = 9 \times 2$

$n =$ 8

8. $16 - 5 = 4 + b$

$b =$ 5

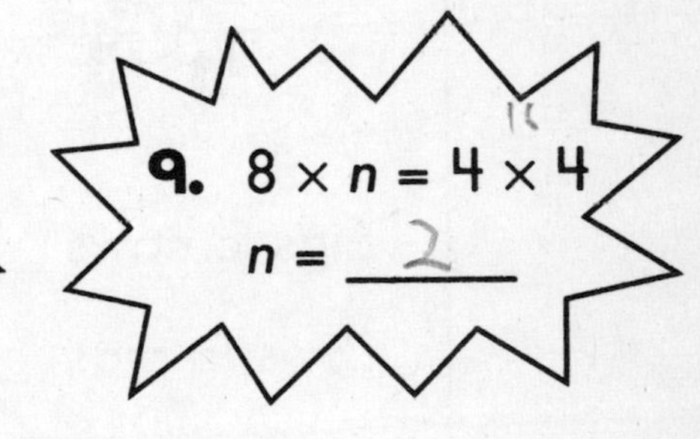

9. $8 \times n = 4 \times 4$

$n =$ 2

10. $25 - t = 2 \times 10$

$t =$ 5

11. $12 \div 4 = 8 - n$

$n =$ 5

12. $m \div 5 = 16 - 12$

$m =$ 4

FAMILY NOTE: Your child is learning to use informal methods to solve equations with one unknown number. Ask your child to explain how he or she solved some of the equations on this page.

Exploring Ratio

Write the ratios for each picture.

1.

triangles to squares 4:7

squares to triangles 7:4

triangles to figures 4:11

2.

dimes to nickels 5:4

nickels to dimes 4:5

nickels to coins 4:9

3.

pigs to cows 6:5

cows to pigs 5:6

cows to animals 5:11

4.

trucks to cars 4:7

cars to trucks 7:4

cars to vehicles 11

Write each ratio in two other ways.

5. 6 to 7 $\frac{6}{7}$ 6:7

6. 2 : 9 $\frac{2}{9}$ 2:9

7. $\frac{3}{5}$ 3 to 5 3:5

8. The ratio of girls to boys in a swimming pool is 3 to 5. How many girls and how many boys might there be in the pool? Give four different possibilities.

3 girls and 5 boys

5 girls and 3 boys

13 girls and 4 boys

25 girls and 4 boys

Draw a picture to show each ratio.

1.	**2.**	**3.**
8 : 11	5 to 6	7 : 4

What does each ratio compare?

4. 3 : 6 c to + ________________

5. 6 : 3 + to C ________________

6. 6 : 9 + to A ________________

7. 3 : 9 A to + ________________

8. 9 : 6 A to ! ________________

9. 9 : 3 A to C ________________

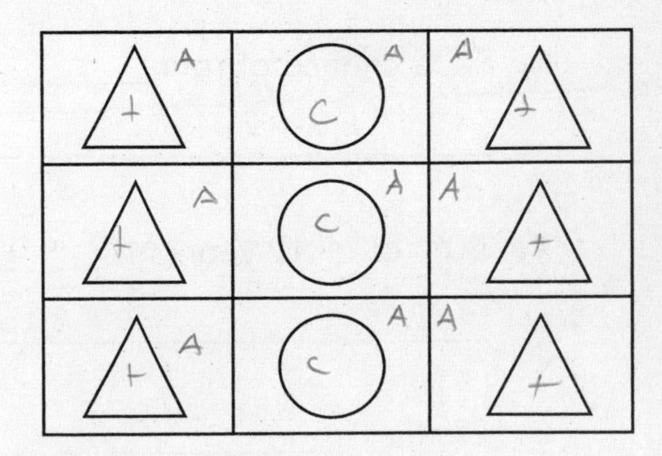

10. The ratio of vowels to consonants in a word is 1 to 3.
How many letters might there be in the word? 4 ______

FAMILY NOTE: Your child is exploring the concept of ratio. Ask your child to describe some everyday uses of ratios. For example, when cooking rice, the ratio might be 2 cups of water to 1 cup of uncooked rice.

Exploring the Uses of Percent

Write each percent in two other ways.

1. 35%

thrith five percent

$\frac{35}{100}$

2. 62 out of 100

62:100

$\frac{62}{100}$

3. twenty-seven percent

$\frac{27}{100}$

27:100

4. 98%

98:100

$\frac{98}{100}$

Write what you think each use of percent means.

5. 30% off all jeans 30% off the regular piece

6. 90% chance of rain 90% of rain

7. 50% of all 12-year-olds 11 and a half years old

8. 2% milk only 2% of ( ) in it

9. 10% more toothpaste more amount of toothpaste

Look through newspapers, flyers, and magazines.
Copy two examples of a percent being used for each purpose.
Write what you think the percent means.

1. A percent used in a weather forecast ______________________

____

____

____

____

2. A percent used in a sale advertisement ______________________

____

____

____

____

3. A percent used in an interest rate ______________________

____

____

____

____

4. A percent that is not a whole number ______________________

____

____

____

____

FAMILY NOTE: Your child is beginning to explore the concept of percent. Help your child look for examples of percents used in different ways. Ask your child to tell you what he or she thinks each percent means.

Showing the Meaning of Percent

Write the percent that describes the shaded part of each grid.

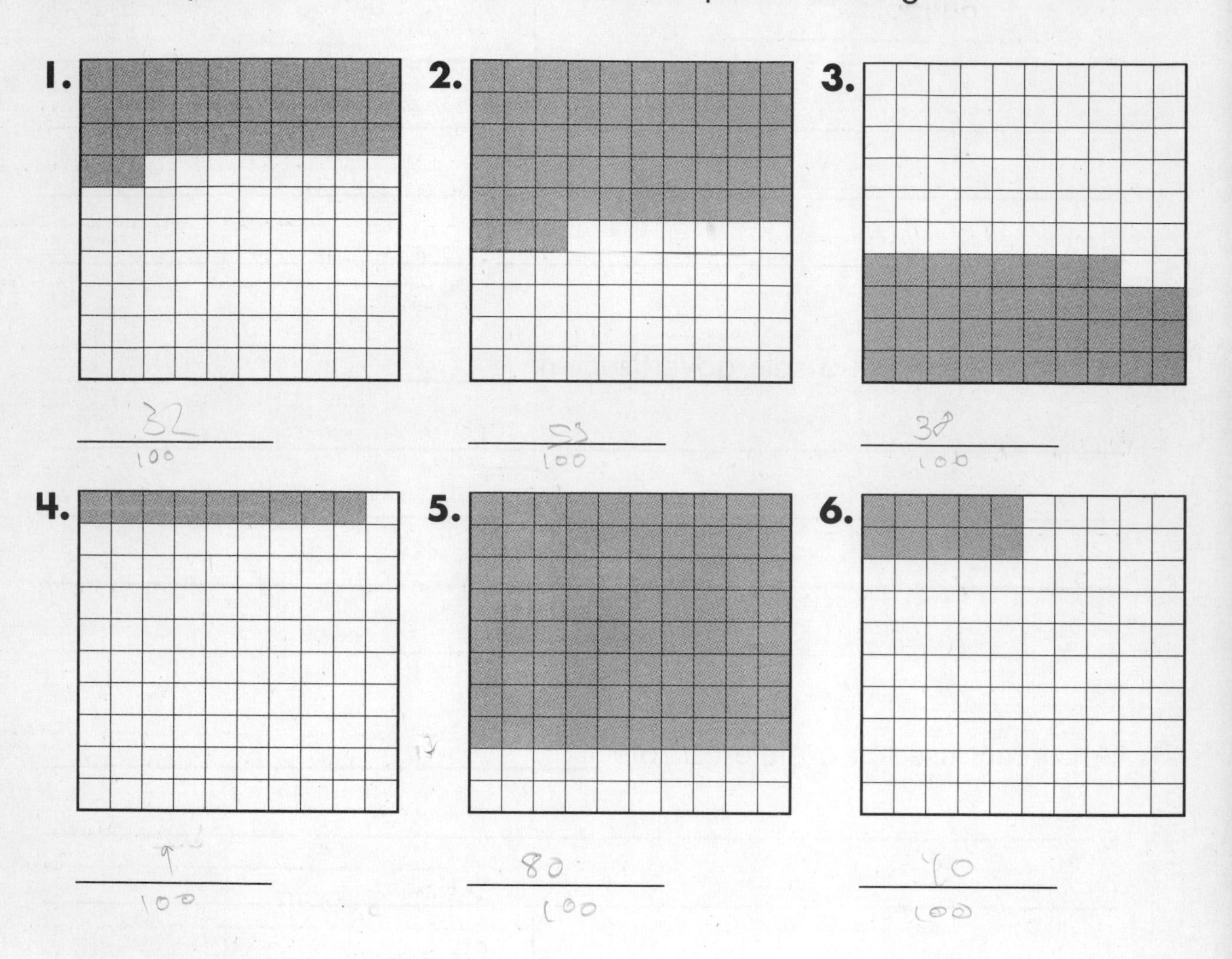

Estimate what percent of each square is shaded.

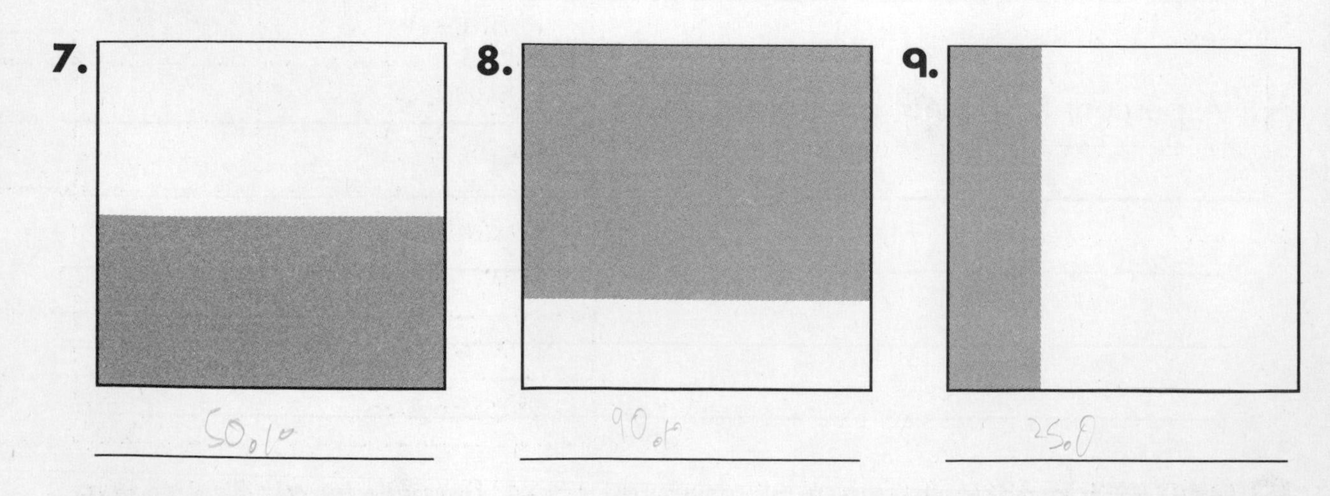

1. Look at the floor plan.
Complete the table to show what percent of the total area is represented by each room.

Bungalow

Bedroom 2
Kitchen
Bathroom
Hallway
Dining Room
Bedroom 1
Living Room

Bungalow

Room	Number of Squares	Percent of Total Area
Kitchen	18	18%
Dining room	15	15%
Living room	20	20%
Bedroom 1	16	16%
Bathroom	8	8%
Bedroom 2	16	16%
Hallway	7	7%

2. Design a floor plan for a doctor's office that includes each room shown in the table. Then complete the table.

Doctor's Office

Room	Number of Squares	Percent of Total Area
Waiting room	10	10%
Reception	10	10%
Examination room 1	20	20%
Examination room 2	20	20%
Examination room 3	10	10%
Hallway	10	10%
Washroom	20	20%

FAMILY NOTE: Your child is learning that percent means "out of one hundred." Interpreting and designing floor plans using a 10×10 grid helps your child understand this concept.

Relating Percent to the Size of the Whole

Colour 50% of each figure.

1. 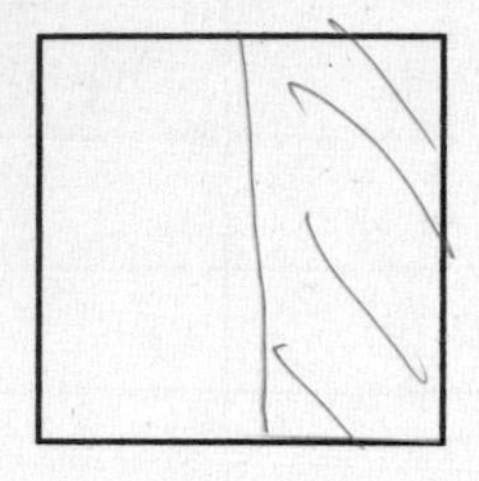

2. 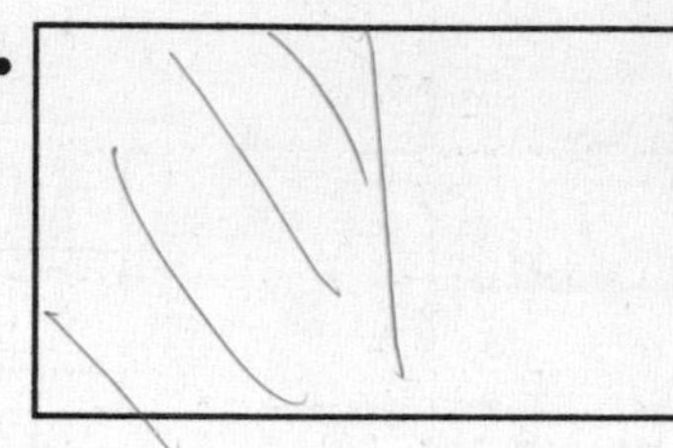

3. 

Colour 75% of each figure.

4. 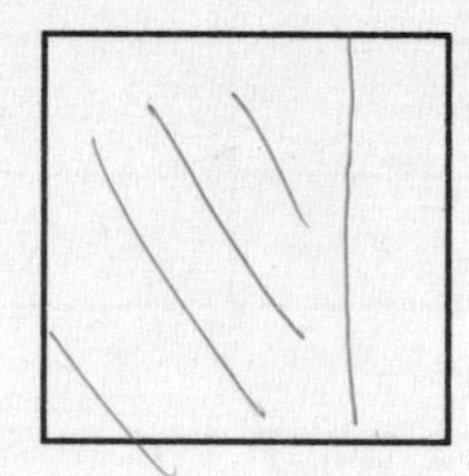

5. 

6. 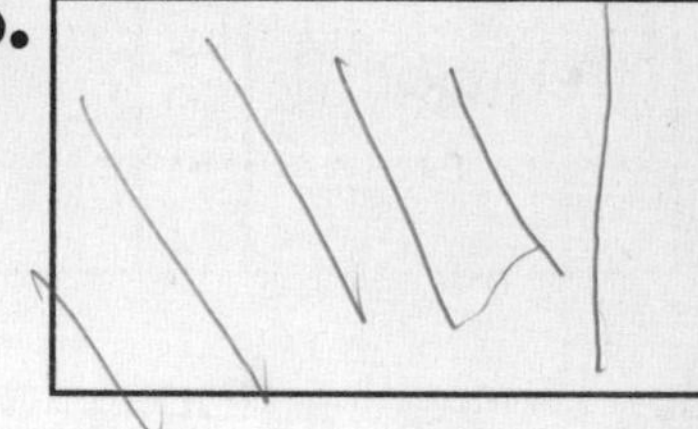

Colour 10% of each figure.

7. 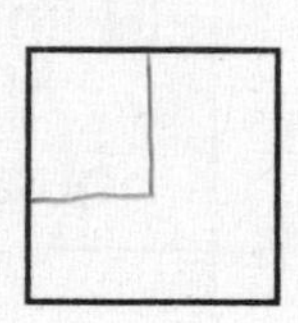

8. 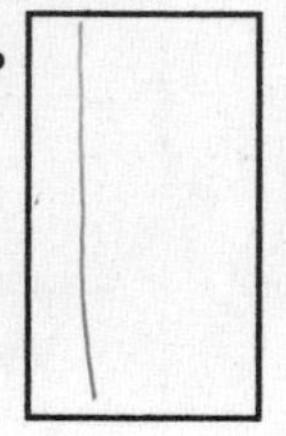

9. 

Colour the rectangle so it is 50% red, 30% green, and 20% yellow.

10. 

Use the data in the table. Make two different floor plans for the office by estimating the amount of floor space needed for each room.

1. The Office

Room or Area	Percent of Floor Space
Office 1	25
Office 2	25
Office 3	20
Washroom	10
Meeting room	10
Hallway	10

2.

FAMILY NOTE: Your child is learning that percent is relative to the size of the whole. As your child completes the floor plans, ask him or her to explain why 25% of the rectangle covers more space than 25% of the square.

Using a Number Line Model for Percent

Estimate to label marks that show 25%, 50%, and 75% of each line segment.

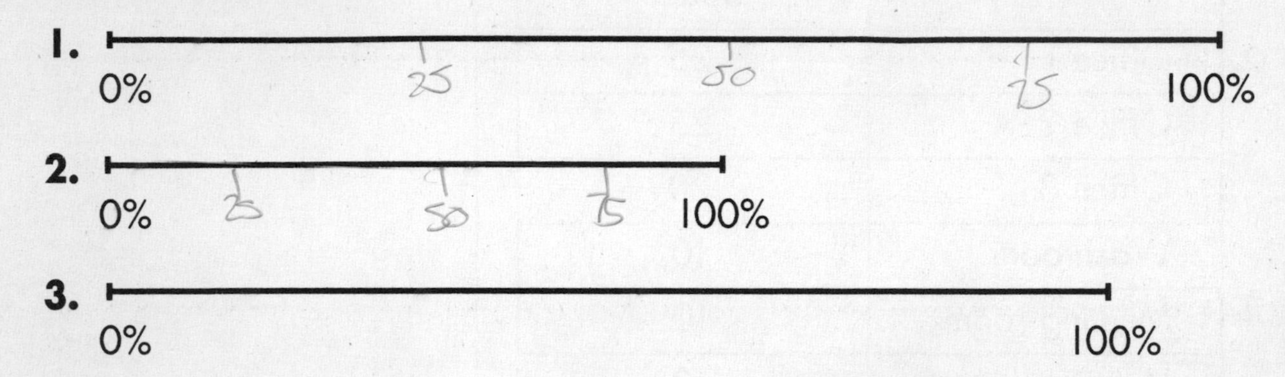

Estimate to label marks that show 33% and 66% of each line segment.

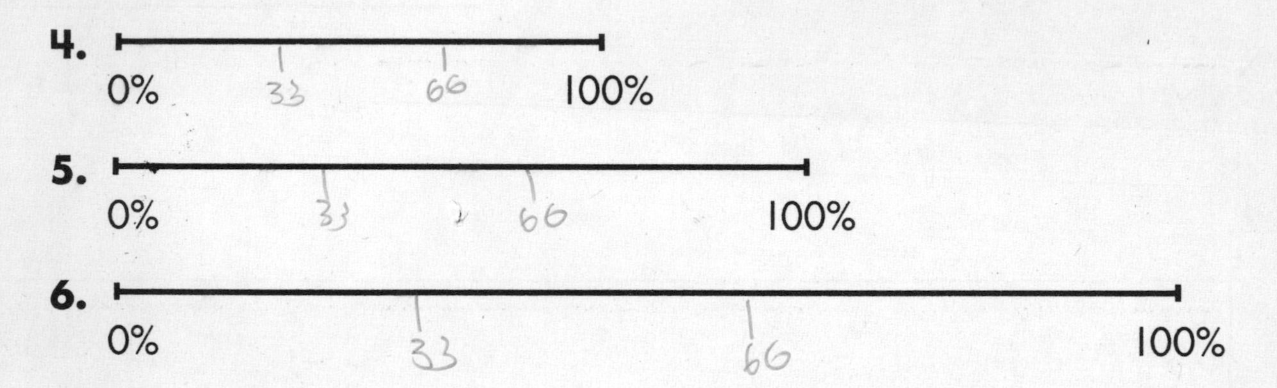

Label the 100% mark for each line segment.

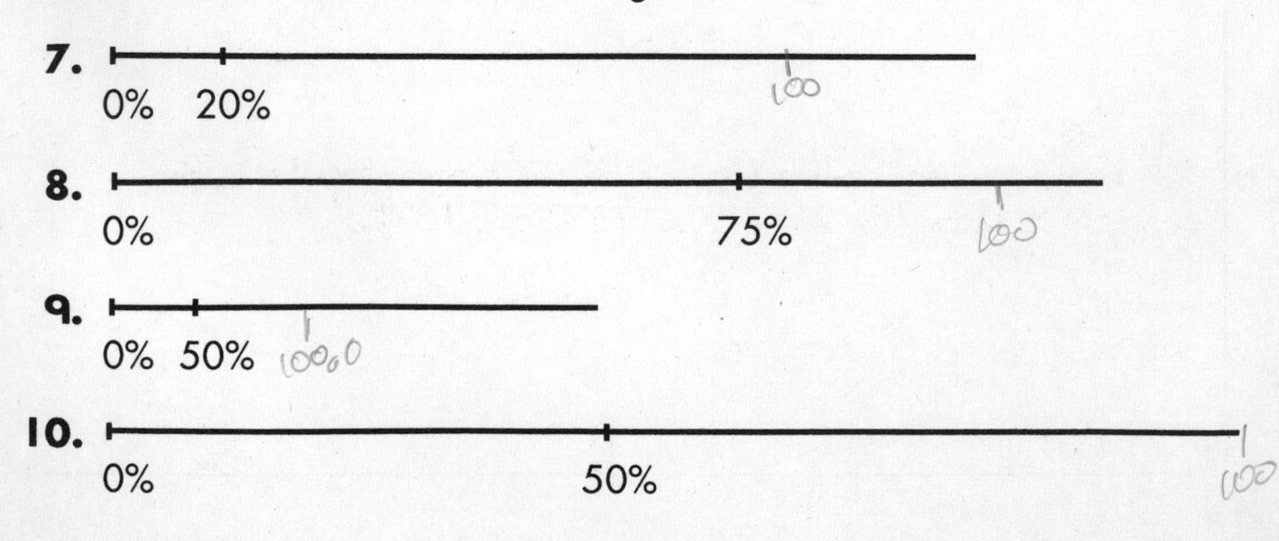

Estimate the percent of the line represented by each mark.

1.

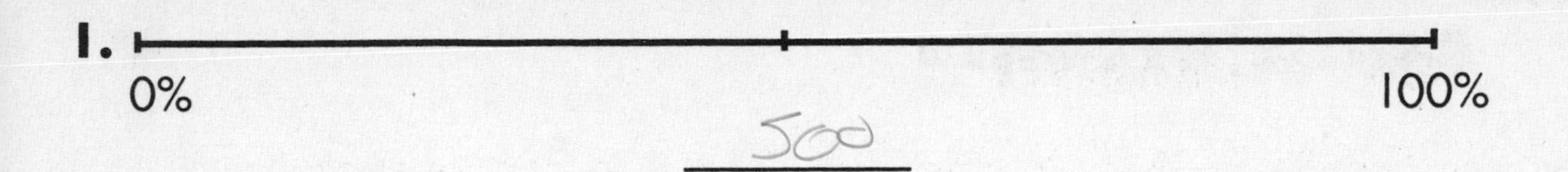

2.

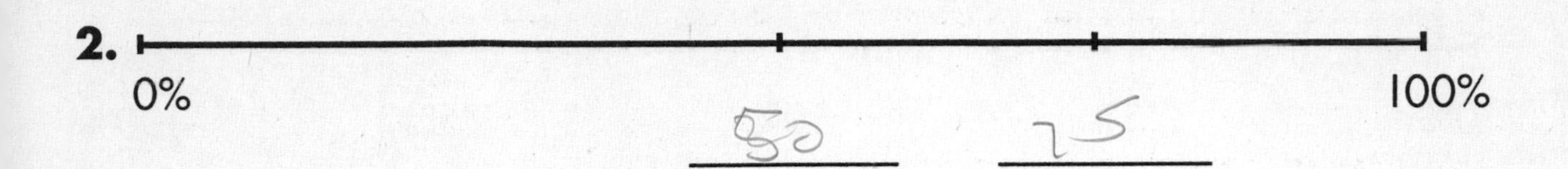

3.

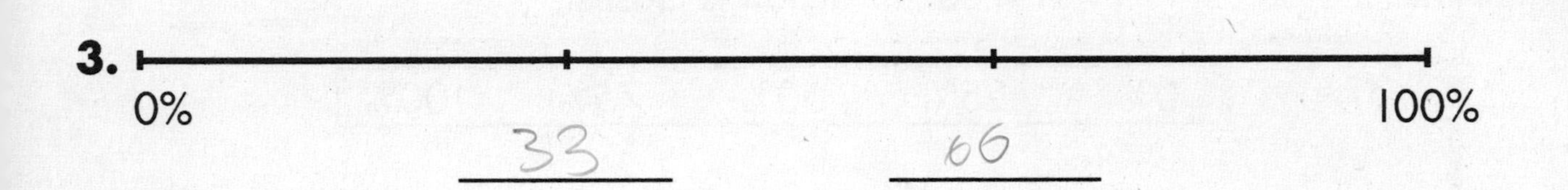

4.

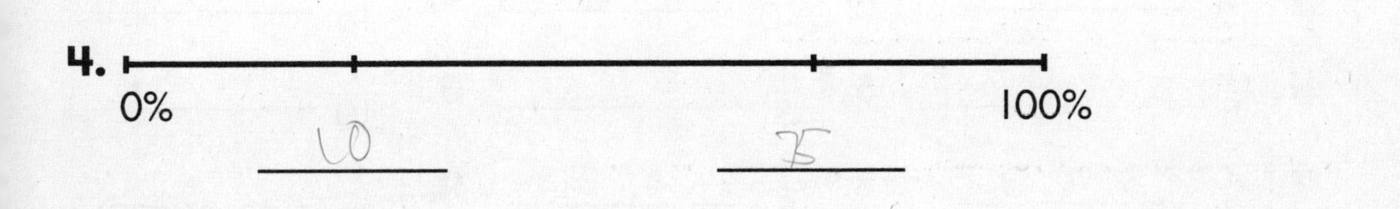

5.

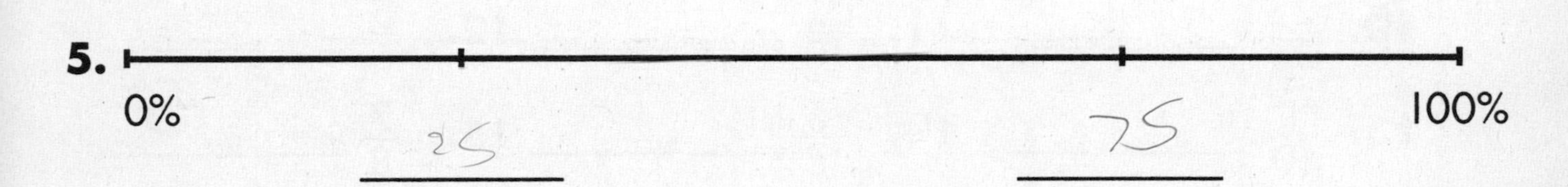

6. Use a ruler to draw a line segment of any length. Label the line segment to show 0%, 25%, 50%, 75%, and 100%.

FAMILY NOTE: Your child is learning to use a linear model for percent. Ask your child to explain how she or he is making the estimates.

Connecting Fractions and Percents

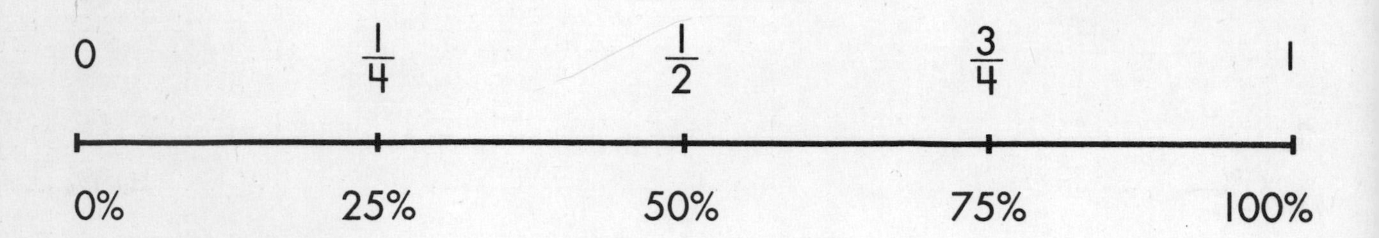

Write the percent to which each fraction is closest.

0%	25%	50%	75%	100%

1. $\frac{1}{12}$ ________ **2.** $\frac{6}{10}$ ________ **3.** $\frac{1}{16}$ ________

4. $\frac{1}{5}$ ________ **5.** $\frac{1}{3}$ ________ **6.** $\frac{7}{10}$ ________

7. $\frac{2}{3}$ ________ **8.** $\frac{4}{5}$ ________ **9.** $\frac{3}{5}$ ________

10. $\frac{2}{5}$ ________ **11.** $\frac{9}{10}$ ________ **12.** $\frac{5}{6}$ ________

13. $\frac{1}{10}$ ________ **14.** $\frac{15}{16}$ ________ **15.** $\frac{7}{8}$ ________

Write the fraction to which each percent is closest.

$\frac{1}{8}$	$\frac{1}{4}$	$\frac{1}{3}$	$\frac{1}{2}$	$\frac{2}{3}$	$\frac{3}{4}$

16. 10% ________ **17.** 72% ________ **18.** 34% ________

19. 51% ________ **20.** 23% ________ **21.** 74% ________

22. 66% ________ **23.** 15% ________ **24.** 49% ________

Write a fraction and a percent to describe the shaded part of each grid.

1.

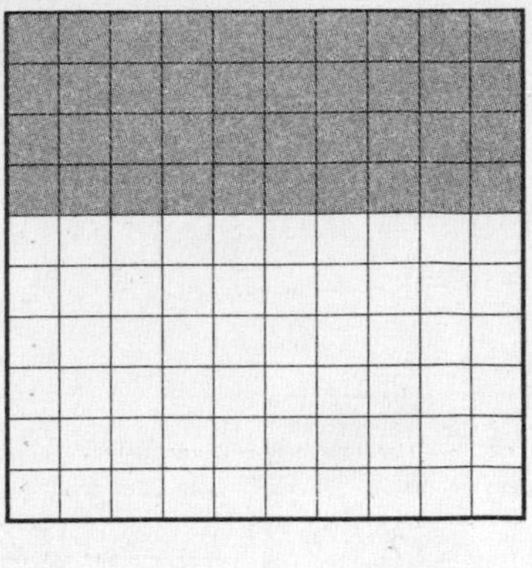

2.

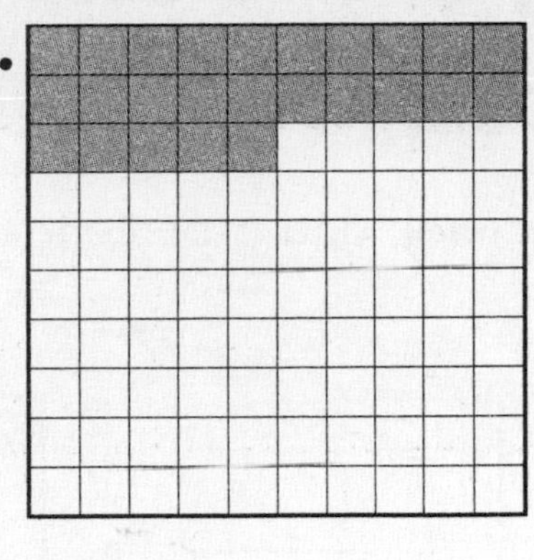

3.

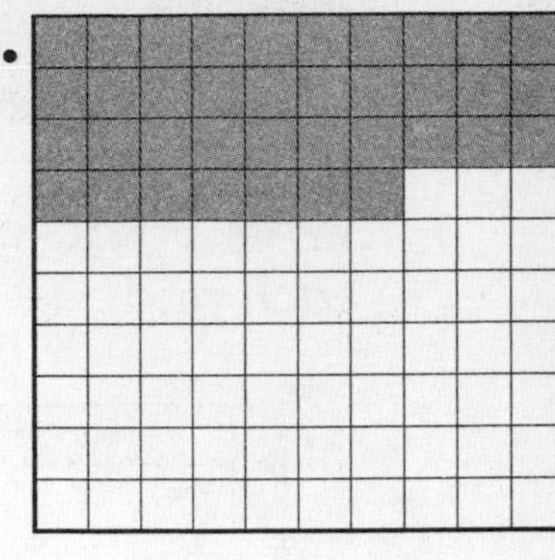

4.

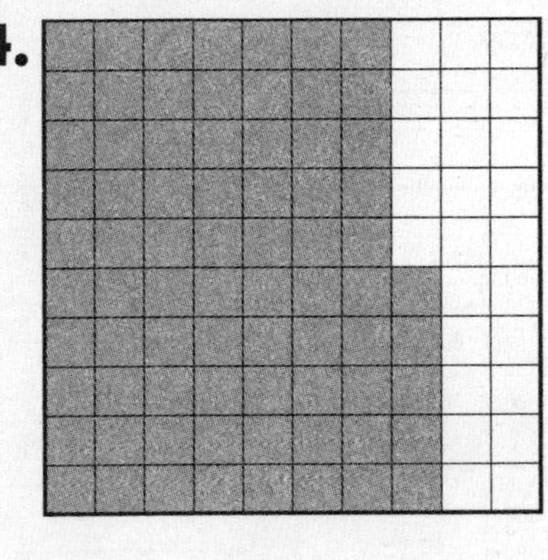

5.

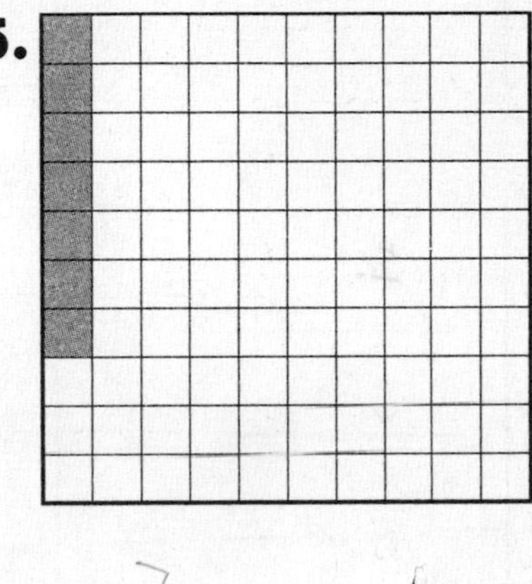

6.

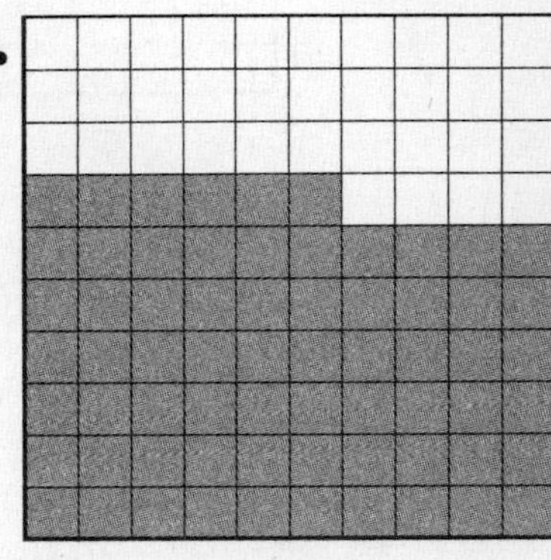

Shade the fraction.
Write the matching percent.

7.

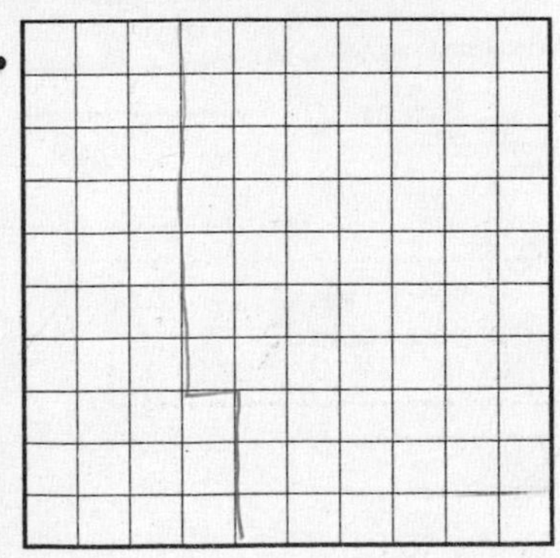

About $\frac{1}{3}$ ______

8.

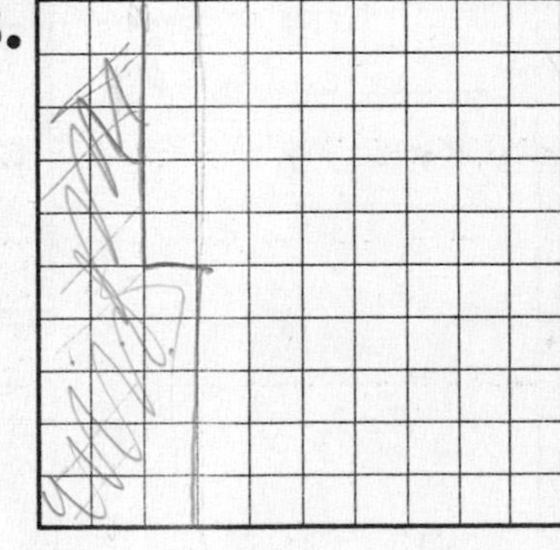

$\frac{1}{5}$ ______

9.

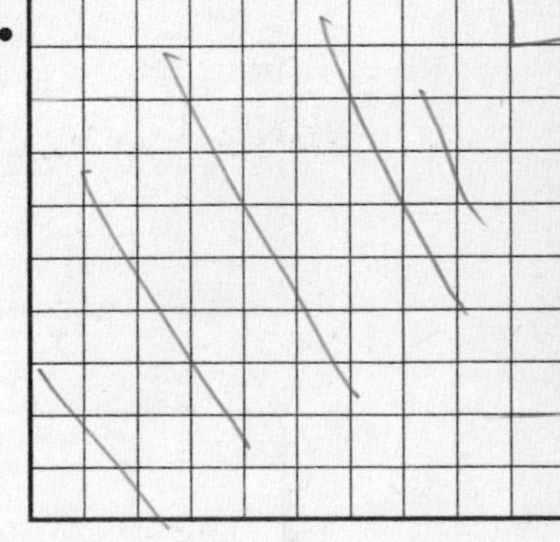

$\frac{99}{100}$ ______

FAMILY NOTE: Your child is learning to make connections between fractions and percents. In completing Problems 1 to 6, encourage your child to write the fractions in simplest terms. For example, reduce $\frac{40}{100}$ to $\frac{2}{5}$.

Exploring Fraction, Decimal, and Percent Equivalents

Write a fraction, a decimal, and a percent to describe the shaded part of each grid.

1.

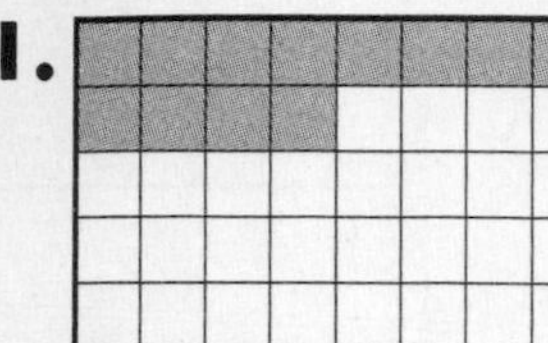

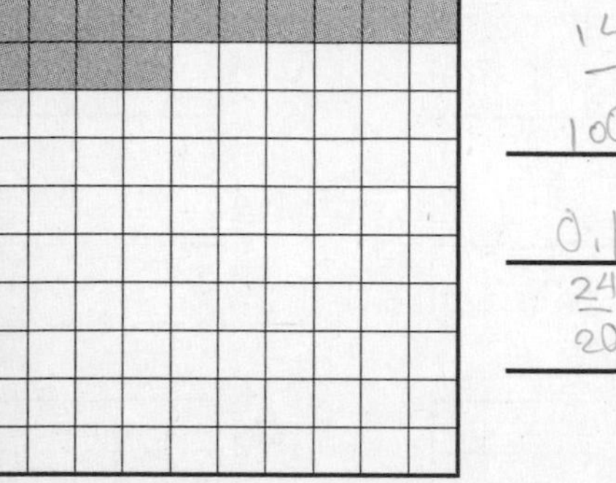

$\frac{14}{100}$

0.14

$\frac{24}{200}$

2.

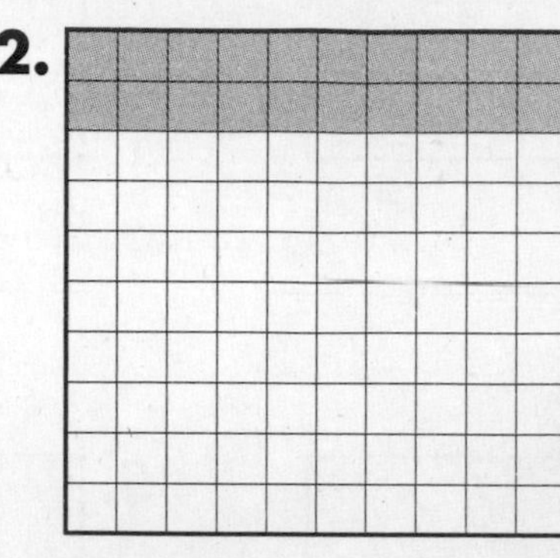

$\frac{20}{200}$

$\frac{40}{100}$

0.20

3.

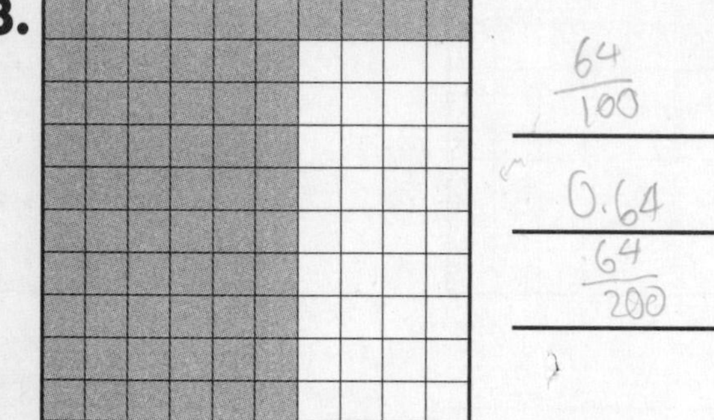

$\frac{64}{100}$

0.64

$\frac{64}{200}$

4.

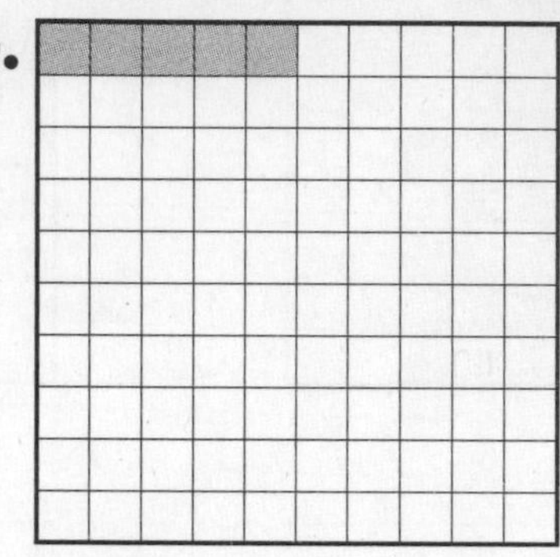

0.05

$\frac{5}{100}$

$\frac{50}{100}$

5.

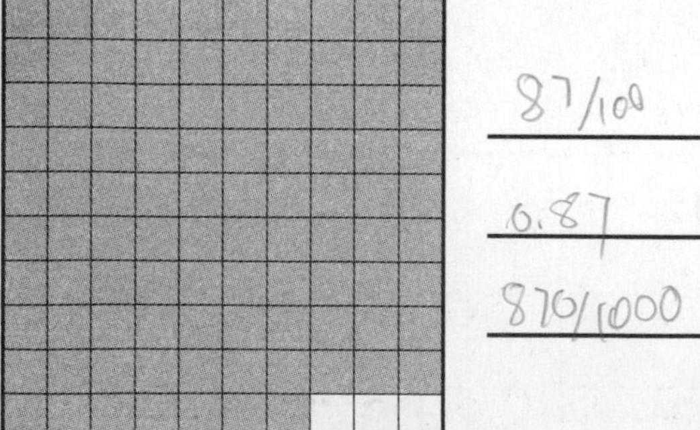

87/100

0.87

870/1000

6.

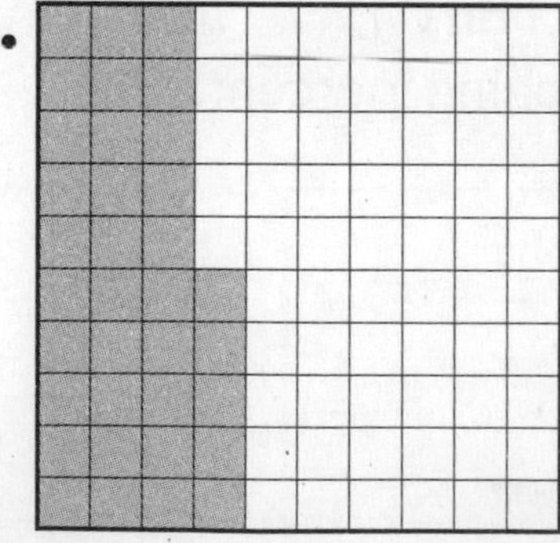

$\frac{35}{100}$

$\frac{70}{200}$

0.35

7.

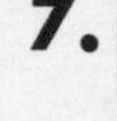

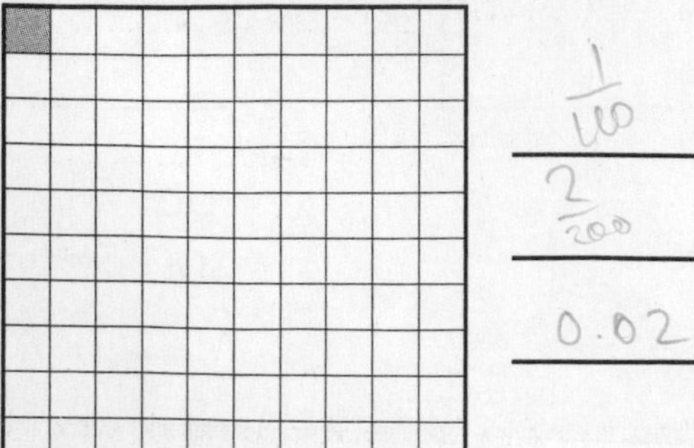

$\frac{1}{100}$

$\frac{2}{200}$

0.02

8.

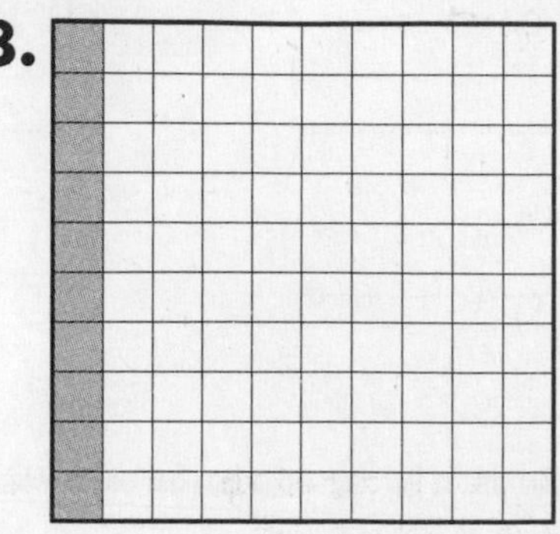

$\frac{10}{100}$

$\frac{20}{200}$

0.10

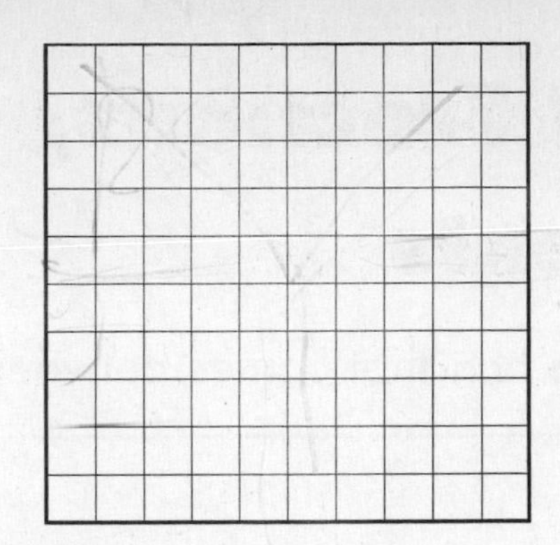

Suppose the grid of 100 squares represents 200 people.
Tell how many people are represented by:

1. 1 square ____________

2. 10 squares ____________

3. 25 squares ____________

4. 75 squares ____________

5. 0.5 of the grid ____________

6. 0.01 of the grid ____________

7. 0.70 of the grid ____________

8. 0.1 of the grid ____________

9. $\frac{1}{10}$ of the grid ____________

10. $\frac{1}{4}$ of the grid ____________

11. $\frac{3}{4}$ of the grid ____________

12. $\frac{9}{10}$ of the grid ____________

Suppose the grid of 100 squares represents 1000 people.
Tell how many people are represented by:

13. 1 square ____________

14. 50 squares ____________

15. 20 squares ____________

16. 89 squares ____________

17. 0.01 of the grid ____________

18. 0.25 of the grid ____________

19. 0.6 of the grid ____________

20. 0.10 of the grid ____________

21. $\frac{1}{4}$ of the grid ____________

22. $\frac{1}{5}$ of the grid ____________

23. $\frac{1}{2}$ of the grid ____________

24. $\frac{2}{3}$ of the grid ____________

FAMILY NOTE: The work on this page will help to further your child's understanding of percent as a ratio. Your child will see, for example, that 50% could mean 50 out of 100, 100 out of 200, or 500 out of 1000.

Comparing Fractions, Decimals, and Percents

Choose a number from the box that comes between the two given numbers.

$\frac{1}{4}$	$\frac{1}{2}$	$\frac{3}{4}$	$\frac{1}{10}$	$\frac{2}{3}$	$\frac{9}{10}$

1. 0.86, $\frac{9}{10}$, 98%

2. 23%, $\frac{1}{4}$, 0.3

3. 70%, $\frac{3}{4}$, 0.80

4. 0.01, $\frac{1}{10}$, 14%

5. 60%, $\frac{2}{3}$, 0.70

6. 0.45, $\frac{1}{2}$, 0.53

0.15	0.35	0.75	0.61	0.90	0.99

7. $\frac{7}{10}$, 0.75, 80%

8. 88%, 0.90, $\frac{93}{100}$

9. 32%, 0.35, $\frac{2}{5}$

10. $\frac{9}{10}$, 0.99, 100%

11. 12%, 0.15, $\frac{1}{5}$

12. $\frac{1}{2}$, 0.61, 65%

12%	70%	25%	50%	42%	83%

13. $\frac{1}{10}$, 12%, 0.14

14. 0.40, 42%, $\frac{1}{2}$

15. $\frac{47}{100}$, 50%, 0.59

16. $\frac{4}{5}$, 83%, 0.90

17. 0.68, 70%, $\frac{3}{4}$

18. $\frac{1}{5}$, 25%, 0.27

Write >, <, or =.

1. $\frac{1}{2}$ ___ 25%
2. 45% ___ 0.75
3. 0.1 ___ $\frac{1}{10}$
4. 75% ___ $\frac{3}{4}$
5. $\frac{7}{10}$ ___ 0.85
6. $\frac{2}{3}$ ___ 60%
7. $\frac{9}{10}$ ___ 98%
8. 85% ___ $\frac{85}{100}$
9. 16% ___ $\frac{1}{10}$
10. 0.24 ___ 21%
11. $\frac{5}{8}$ ___ 0.5
12. 25% ___ $\frac{1}{4}$
13. $\frac{3}{5}$ ___ 60%
14. 0.45 ___ 40%
15. 90% ___ 0.9

Write the numbers in order from least to greatest.

16. 16%, $\frac{7}{100}$, 0.13

___

17. 92%, 0.9, $\frac{94}{100}$

___

18. $\frac{1}{2}$, 45%, 0.2

___

19. $\frac{4}{5}$, 89%, 0.39

___

20. 30%, $\frac{1}{3}$, 0.37

___

21. 0.87, 90%, $\frac{89}{100}$

___

22. $\frac{2}{3}$, 50%, 0.62

___

23. 15%, $\frac{7}{10}$, 0.12

___

FAMILY NOTE: Your child has been learning about fraction, decimal, and percent equivalents. To help your child with this page, you might ask him or her to mentally convert the numbers in each problem to the same form for easier comparison.

Exploring Integers

Temperature Ranges for March 24			
City	High/Low (°C)	City	High/Low (°C)
Calgary	8/–5	Quebec City	–5/–14
Charlottetown	0/–5	Regina	2/–14
Edmonton	6/–9	St. John's	0/–4
Fredericton	–3/–8	Toronto	2/–8
Halifax	2/–3	Vancouver	14/–1
Inuvik	0/–9	Victoria	15/4
Montreal	–3/–12	Whitehorse	1/–13
North Bay	–9/–13	Winnipeg	–8/–12
Ottawa	–4/–11	Yellowknife	–9/–24

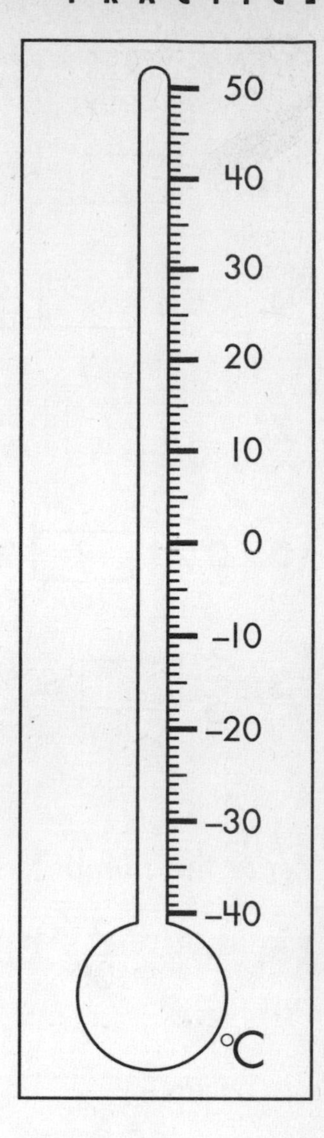

Use the chart and the thermometer.
Find and record the temperature difference for each city.

1. Calgary 8+/5-

2. Charlottetown 0/5

3. Edmonton 6/9-

4. Fredericton -3 -8

5. Halifax 2/3-

6. Inuvik 0/-9

7. Montreal -3/-12

8. North Bay -9/13

9. Ottawa -4/-11

10. Quebec City 5-14

11. Regina 2/-14

12. St. John's 0/-4

13. Toronto 2+ -8

14. Vancouver 14/-1

15. Victoria 15/4

16. Whitehorse 1+/-13

17. Winnipeg -8/-12

18. Yellowknife -9/24

19. An extreme change in temperature took place in January, 1962, in Pincher Creek, Alberta. The temperature rose from –19°C to 22°C in one hour!

What temperature difference was this? 3 C

Each diagram shows the highest and lowest temperatures for one year in one Canadian city.

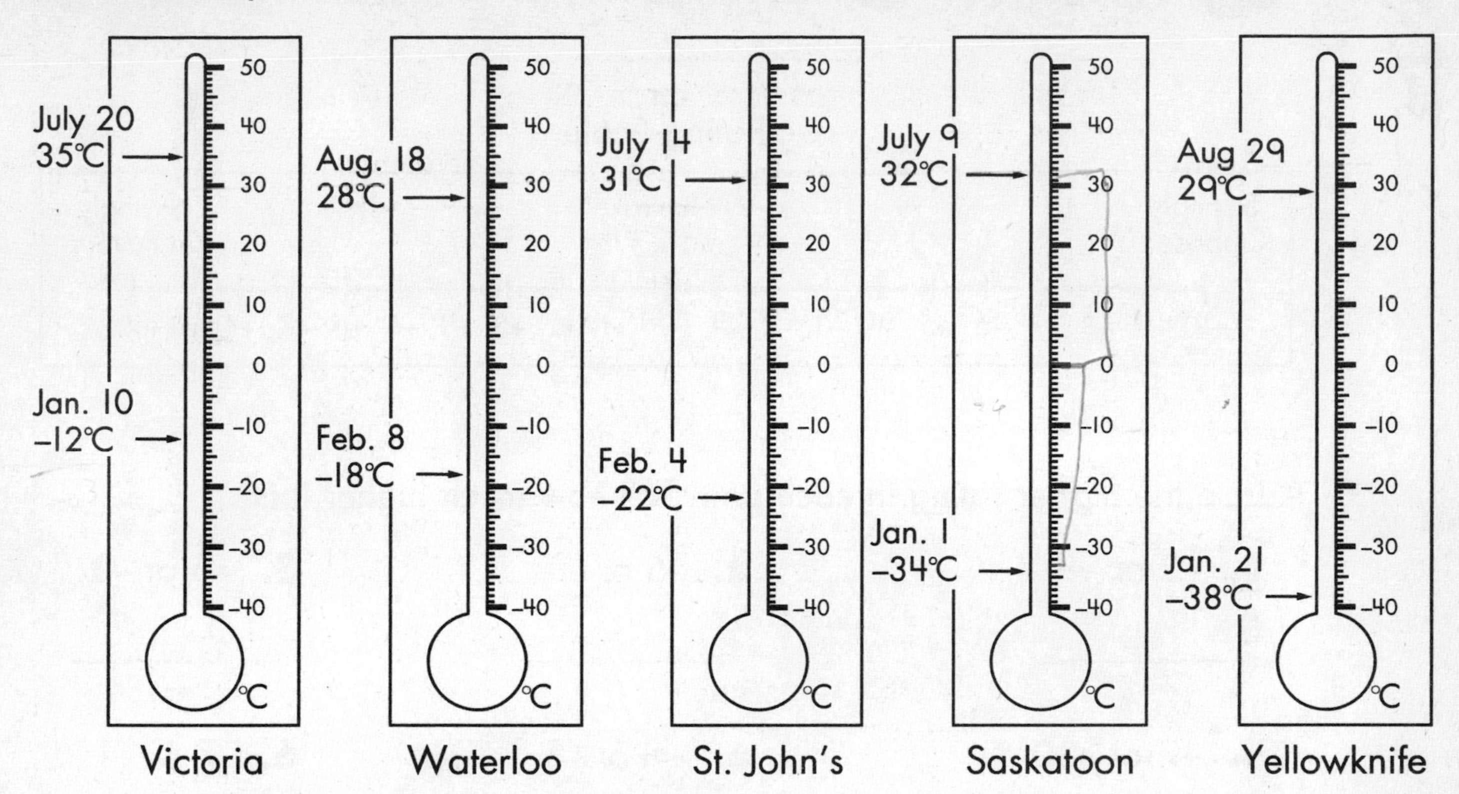

Find and record the temperature difference for each city.

1. Victoria 23 ________ **2.** Waterloo 10 ________ **3.** St. John's 8 ________

4. Saskatoon ________ **5.** Yellowknife ________

6. Order the above cities from least to greatest temperature difference.

____

Order each set of temperatures from lowest to highest.

7. 8°C, –4°C, 0°C

-4, 0°C, 8+ ________________

8. –13°C, 14°C, –9°C

-13, -9, 14+ ________________

9. 5°C, 9°C, –2°C

-2, +5 +9 ________________

10. –3°C, –27°C, 6°C

-27, -3, 6+ ________________

FAMILY NOTE: Your child is learning about negative numbers. The thermometer provides a visual way for your child to think about these numbers. In mathematics, the words "negative ten degrees Celsius" are used more than the informal "minus ten" or "ten below zero."

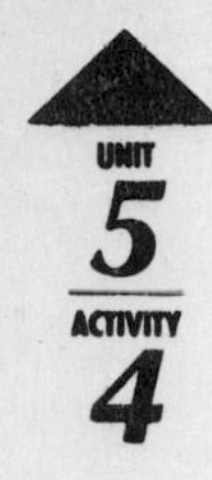

Comparing Integers

Rating Scale

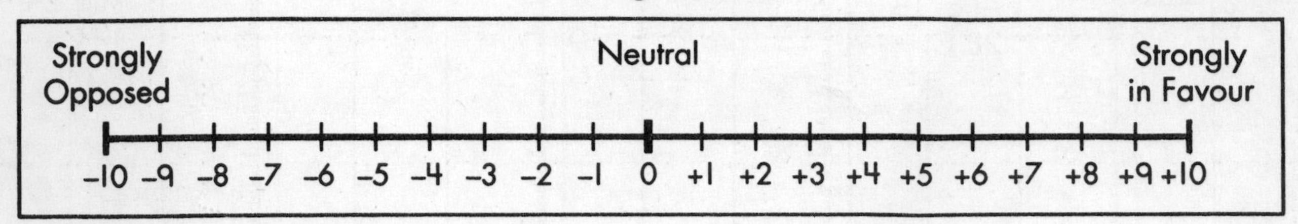

Circle the higher rating in each pair. Tell how much higher it is.

1. −2 or +4

4+ ______

2. −6 or −8

-6 ______

3. +5 or −3

+5 ______

4. +7 or +10

+10 ______

5. +9 or −3

+9 ______

6. −7 or +1

+1 ______

7. 0 or −2

0 ______

8. −3 or −7

-3 ______

9. +1 or 0

+1 ______

Circle the lower rating in each pair. Tell how much lower it is.

10. −8 or −2

-8 ______

11. 0 or +2

0 ______

12. −5 or 0

-5 ______

13. +3 or −9

-9 ______

14. −10 or −7

-10 ______

15. −3 or +4

-3 ______

16. −4 or −6

-6 ______

17. +8 or +6

+6 ______

18. 0 or −3

-3 ______

1. Use the rating scale to tell how you feel about each statement. Ask a friend or family member to do the same. Record your ratings in the chart.

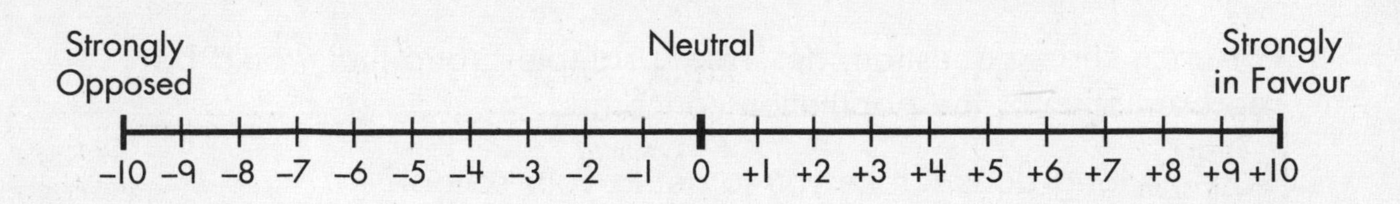

	My Rating	My Partner's Rating
1. Cats should be required to wear leashes.	−10	−10
2. Hockey is a great spectator sport.	−10	−10
3. All Grade 6 students should do homework every night.	−10	−9
4. More mathematics should be taught in school.	−10	−10
5. Schools should provide free snacks at recess.	+10	+10
6. Pizza delivery should always be free.	+10	+10

2. For each statement, tell whose rating was higher, and how much higher it was.

	Whose rating was higher?	How much higher?
Statement 1:	= 10−, 10−	=
Statement 2:	= 10−, 10−	=
Statement 3:	= 10−, 9−	1
Statement 4:	= 10−, 10−	=
Statement 5:	= 10+, 10+	=
Statement 6:	= 10+, 10+	=

FAMILY NOTE: Your child is learning to use positive and negative integers on a rating scale. Ask your child to explain how she or he determines how much higher one rating is over the other.

Sampling

For each survey question, describe a sample group that would be representative of the population concerned.

1. How long does it take you to get to your school?

____

____

2. Should students attend school all year round?

____

____

3. Should Remembrance Day be a school holiday?

____

____

4. Should dog owners have to buy licences for their pets?

____

____

5. Write a survey question like the questions above.

____

____

6. Describe a non-biased sample group and a biased sample group for your question.

a) non-biased: ____

____

b) biased: ____

____

For each survey question, describe a biased sample group.

1. Should students be allowed to read comic books in class?

2. Should skateboards be allowed on the playground?

3. Should the city construct bicycle paths through the parks?

4. Should a city worker get a holiday on her or his birthday?

5. Write a survey question like the questions above.

6. Describe a sample group for your question that would not be biased.

FAMILY NOTE: Your child has been introduced to the concept of sampling and has explored some of the factors involved in selecting samples. He or she is learning that a sample group may or may not represent a population in a fair and unbiased way. For Problems 1 to 4 on this page, ask your child to explain why each sample group he or she described is biased.

Taking a Sample

Plan a survey to predict the ratio of right-handed to left-handed students in your school.

1. Write the survey question you will ask.

____

____

2. How many students will be in your sample? ____________

3. How will you choose students to make sure your sample is random?

____

____

4. Conduct your survey. Tally the results in this table.

Right-handed Students	Left-handed Students

5. What is the ratio of right-handed to left-handed students in your sample?

____

6. Do you think your results are representative of the whole school?

Why or why not? ____________________

____

A television talk show host has stated that more people prefer a white car to any other car colour.

Plan a survey of people you know to find out if this is true.

1. Write the survey question you will ask.

____

____

____

2. How many people will be in your sample? ________________

3. How will you choose people to make sure your sample is random?

____

____

____

4. Conduct the survey and analyze your data.
Write your conclusions.

____

____

____

____

____

FAMILY NOTE: Your child is learning to choose a random sample, conduct a survey of the sample group, and analyze the results. Ask your child to explain how he or she knows that the selected sample group is random.

Analyzing Scatterplots

Students were surveyed about how much time they spend listening to the radio each day. The results are shown in the scatterplot.

1. How many students were surveyed? ______________

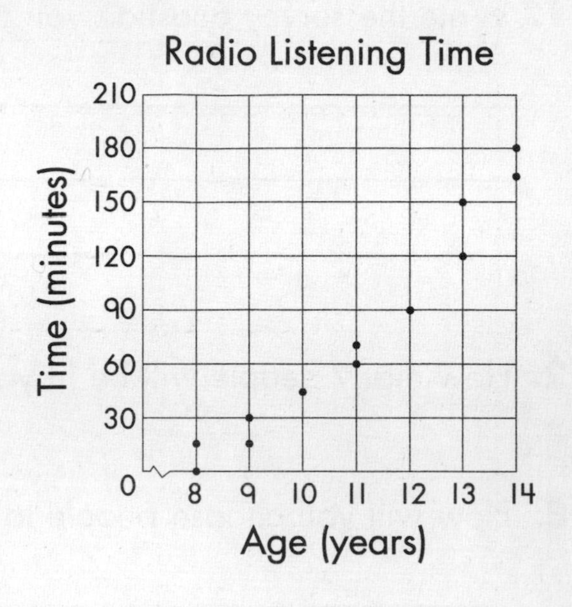

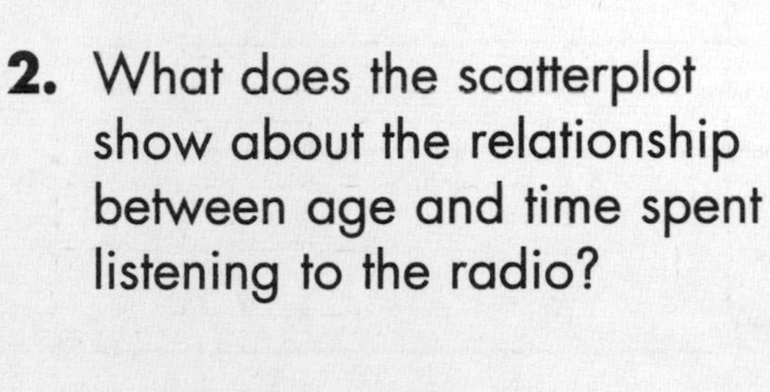

2. What does the scatterplot show about the relationship between age and time spent listening to the radio?

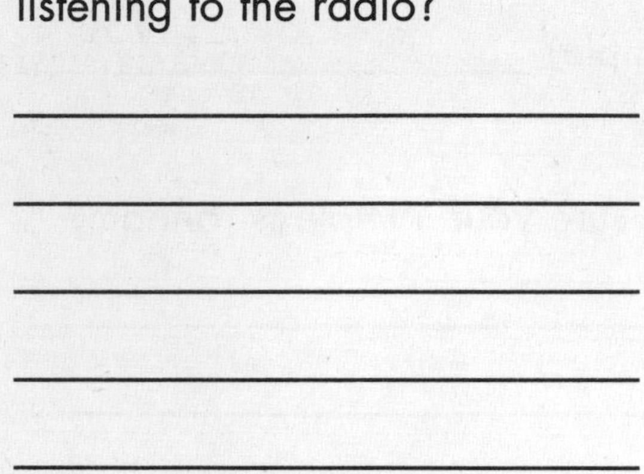

Marissa measured the handspans and hand lengths of some friends. The results are shown in the scatterplot.

3. How many handspans did Marissa measure? ______________

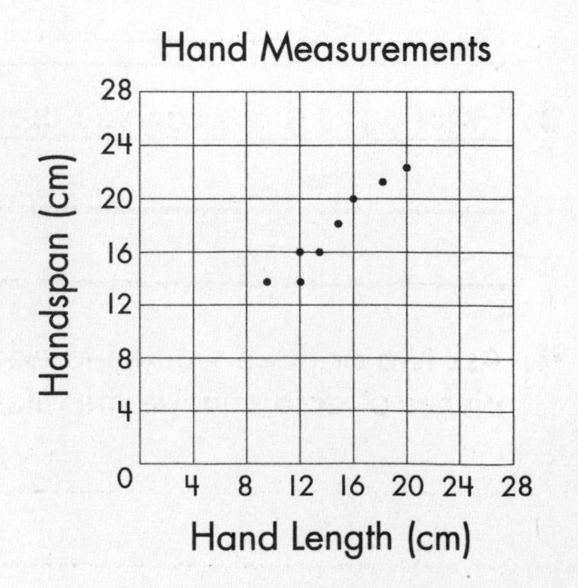

4. What conclusions can Marissa make from the scatterplot?

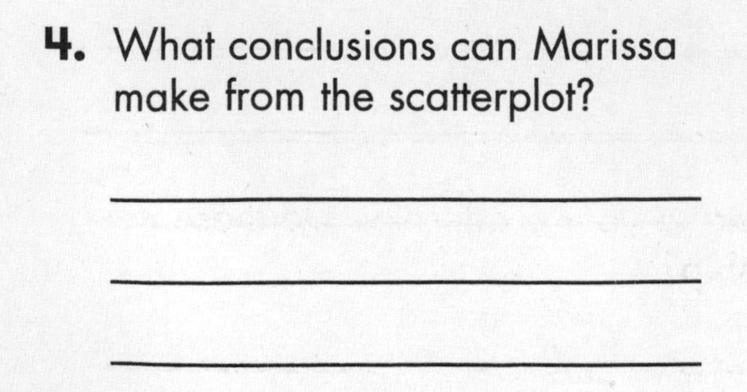

The table below shows the heights and shoe sizes of ten women. Make a scatterplot to display the data.

1.

Height (cm)	Shoe Size
155	6
162	$7\frac{1}{2}$
162	$9\frac{1}{2}$
166	8
161	$7\frac{1}{2}$
168	8
160	6
157	5
170	$8\frac{1}{2}$
154	$5\frac{1}{2}$

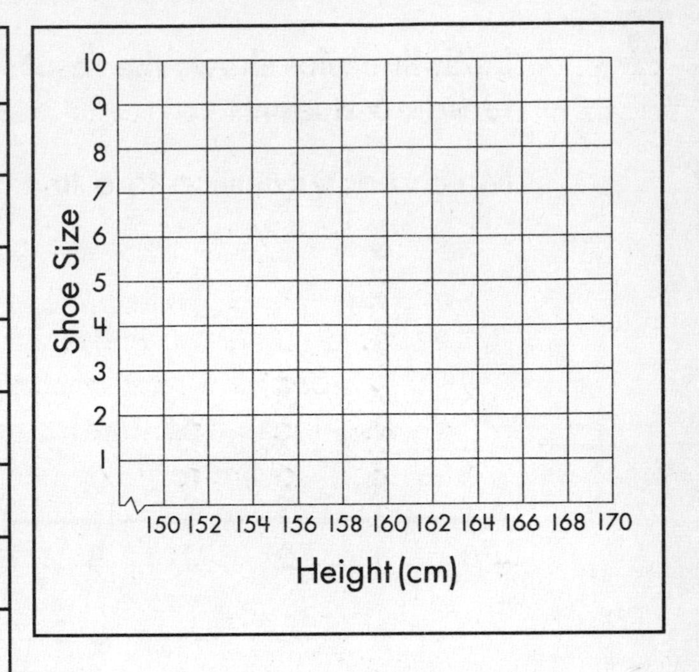

2. Would you expect to find a relationship between the heights of women and their shoe sizes? Why or why not?

____

____

3. What conclusions can you draw from the scatterplot?

____

____

4. Ask two or three women to add data to your scatterplot. Do these new pieces of data change the relationship?

____

____

FAMILY NOTE: Your child is learning to use scatterplots to see if there is a relationship between two quantities. Ask your child to explain how she or he plotted each point on the scatterplot.

Making and Analyzing Line Plots

Each line plot shows the results of a survey question posed to a group of Grade 6 students.

Match each question to a line plot.

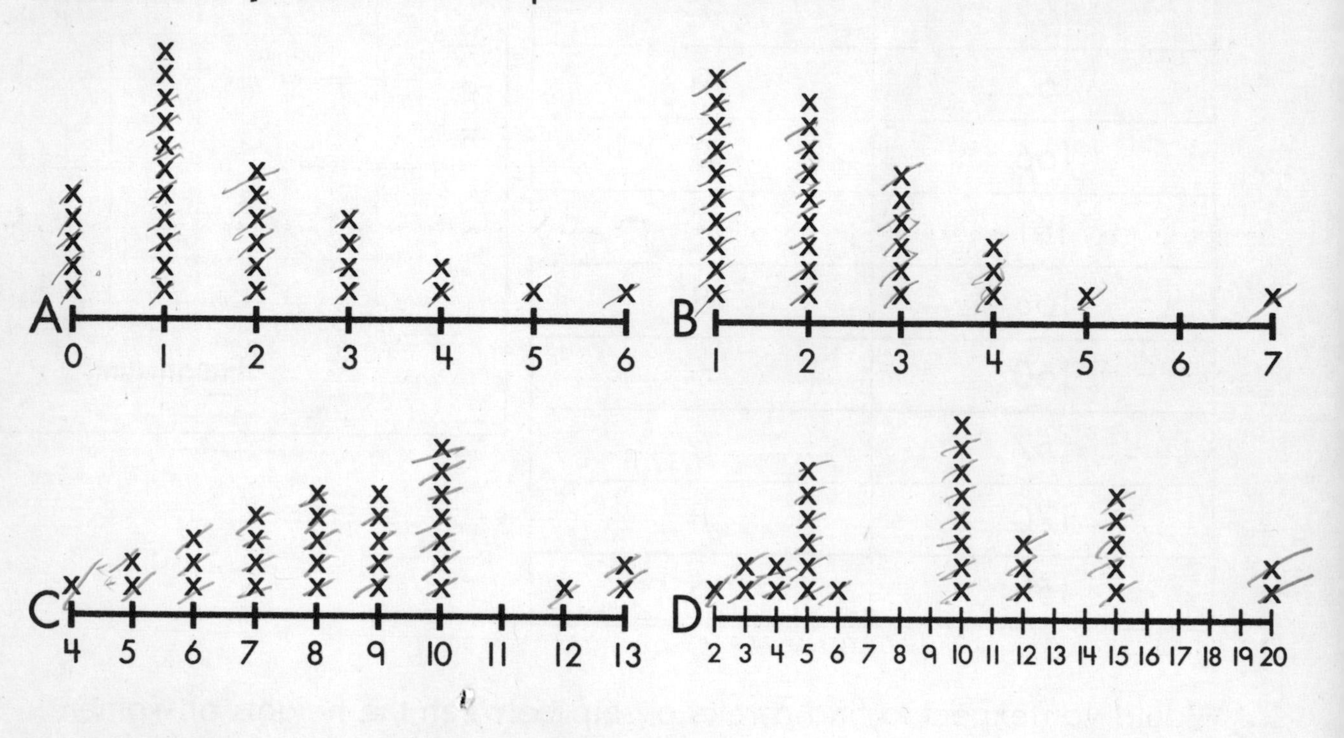

1. How many minutes does it take you to get to school? 2 min

2. How many pets do you have? 0

3. How many children are in your family? 4

4. About how many seconds does it take you to sing "Happy Birthday"? 5 sec

5. Complete the table for the four line plots.

Line Plot	Range	Median	Mode
A	0–6	1	
B	1–7	2	
C	4–13	9	
D	2–20	10	

Each set of data shows the results of a survey of Grade 6 students.
Display each set in a line plot.
Then write a conclusion about each line plot.

1. Number of hours spent reading each week:

1, 4, 3, 4, 4, 1, 5, 1, 7, 2, 1, 4, 3, 3, 6, 5, 5, 4, 2, 1, 6, 5, 3, 2, 8

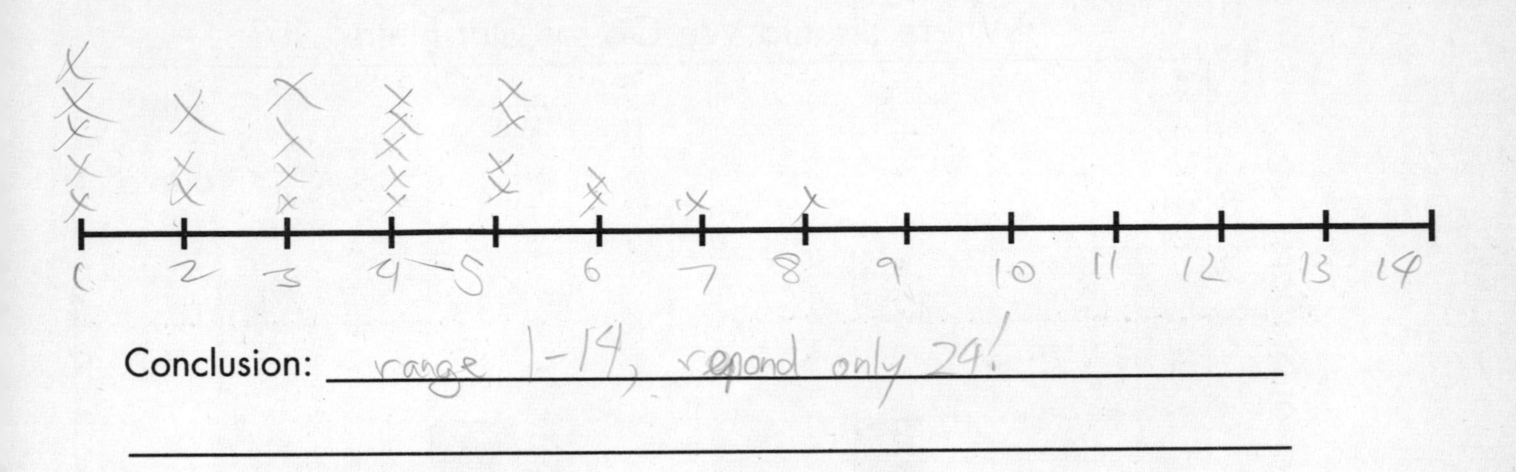

Conclusion: ____________________

____

2. Number of hours spent watching TV each week:

10, 12, 11, 10, 5, 6, 8, 12, 15, 4, 5, 8, 15, 10, 10, 6, 7, 4, 5, 14, 14, 10, 7, 8, 5

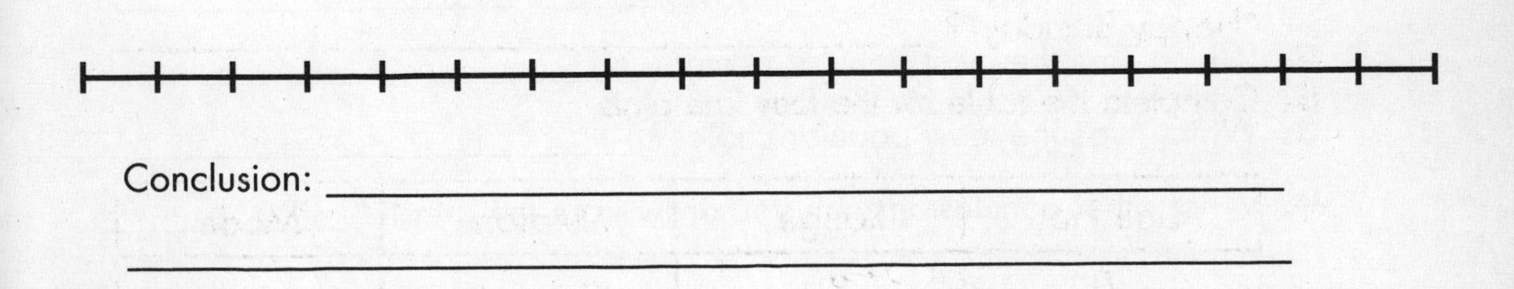

Conclusion: ____________________

____

FAMILY NOTE: Your child is reviewing how to present data in line plots. As your child writes conclusions, encourage him or her to include statements about the range of the data (the difference between the greatest and smallest numbers), the median (the middle number when the numbers are written in order), and the mode (the number that occurs most often).

Making and Analyzing Double-Bar Graphs

The Grades 5 and 6 classes were asked where they should go for their field trip. The double-bar graph displays the results of the survey.

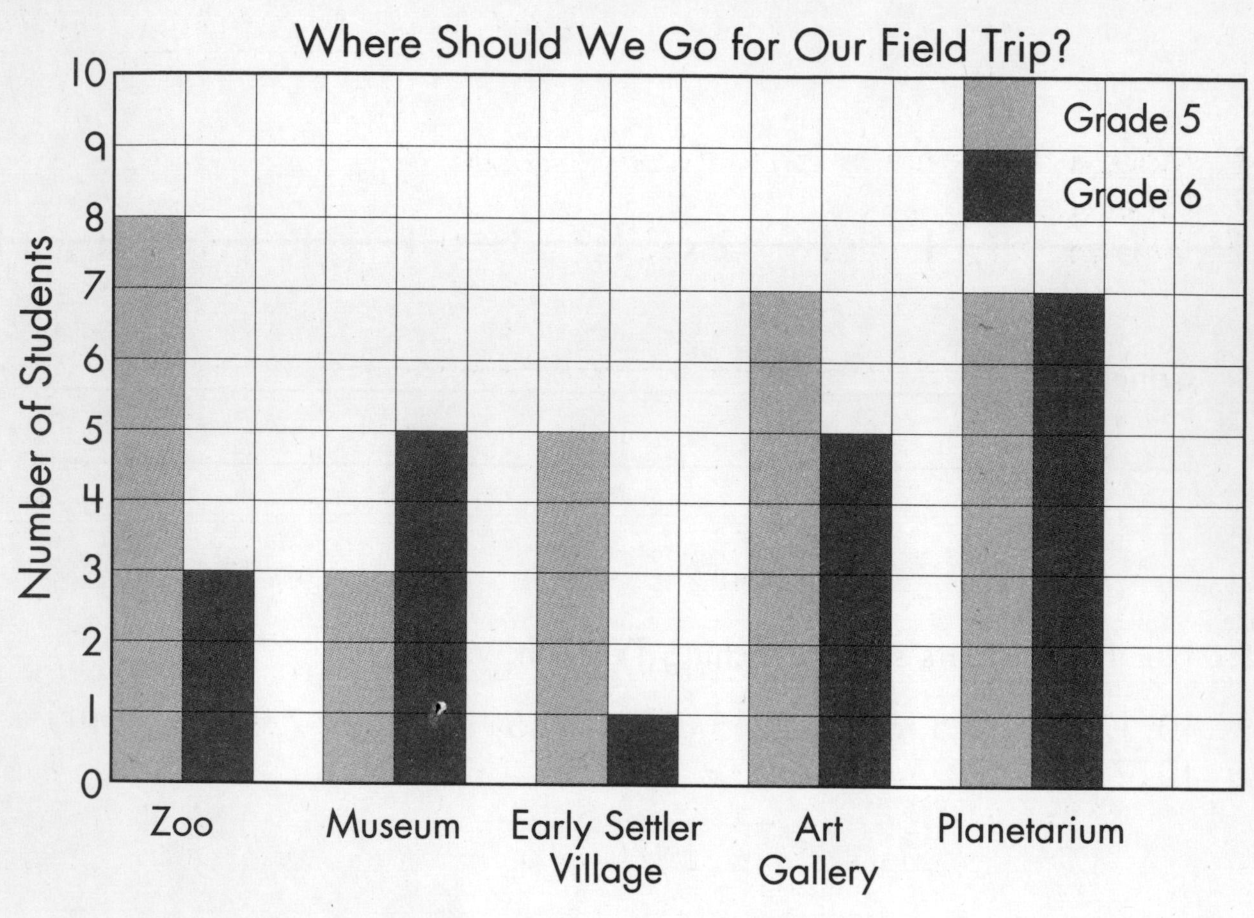

1. How many students were surveyed? 61 _______________

2. Which was the most popular choice? Planetarium _______________

3. Which was the least popular choice? Early Settler Village _______________

4. What other conclusions can you draw from the graph? least like: Early Settler Village, most liked: Planetarium

____

Two groups of students were surveyed about their favourite board game. The tally chart shows the data.

	Grade 5 Students	Grade 6 Students
Chess	卌 |||	卌 卌 |||
Checkers	卌 ||	||
Monopoly	卌 卌 ||||	卌 卌
Trivial Pursuit	卌		卌 卌

1. Make a double-bar graph to display the data.
Label each axis.
Give your graph a title and a key.

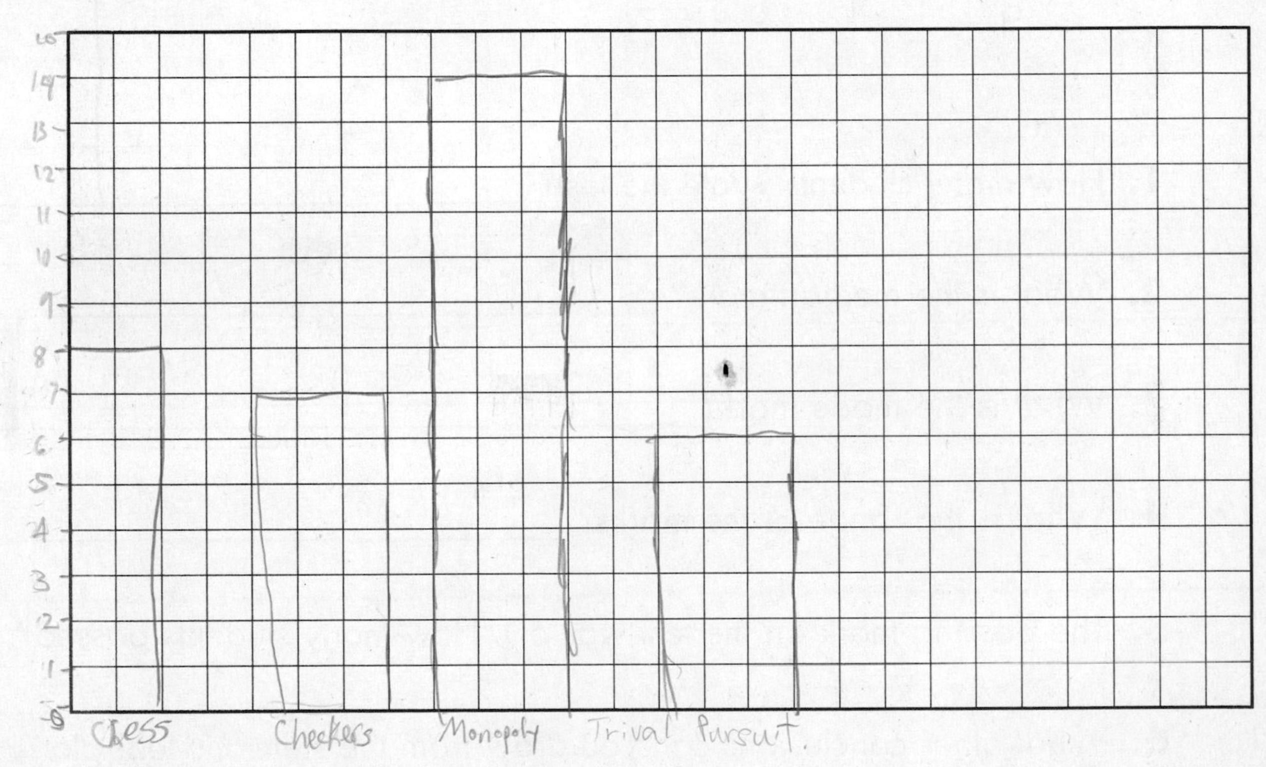

2. How many students were surveyed? 71

3. What conclusions can you draw from the graph?

Everyone likes Monppoly

FAMILY NOTE: Your child is learning how to use a double-bar graph to compare two sets of quantities. Ask your child to explain how he or she decided on the scale for the vertical axis.

Making and Analyzing Stem-and-Leaf Plots

Ms. Wallace has organized her students' math test marks in this stem-and-leaf plot.

Stem	Leaves
4	9
5	2 2
6	0 4 4 5 6 6
7	1 1 2 3 5 7 9 9 9
8	0 2 2 5 6 7 7 8
9	1 4 4 5 7

1. How many students wrote the test? 31

2. What is the median mark? 79

3. What is the mode mark? ____________

4. What is the range of the marks? 49-97

5. The passing mark on the test was 60. How many students passed? 28

6. What other conclusions can you draw from the stem-and-leaf plot?

$\frac{1}{4}$ of the class past.

19/3

Karen asked some of her neighbours and relatives how old they were when they got married. Here are the ages she was given: 25, 19, 24, 21, 22, 35, 16, 21, 31, 43, 29, 19, 21, 23, 26, 31, 40, 33, 17, and 21.

1. Make a stem-and-leaf plot to show Karen's data.
   Arrange the leaves in each row in order from least to greatest.

2. What conclusions can you draw from the stem-and-leaf plot?

   most people are married around when they're 20-32

3. Survey family members and other people you know to find out how old they were when they obtained a driver's licence.
   Make a stem-and-leaf plot to show your data.

4. What conclusions can you draw from your stem-and-leaf plot?

   N/A

FAMILY NOTE: Your child is learning that stem-and-leaf plots are a good way of showing how data are distributed. To help your child analyze the stem-and-leaf plots, ask him or her to consider the range of the data (the difference between the greatest and smallest numbers), the median (the middle number when the numbers are written in order), and the mode (the number that occurs most often).

Choosing an Appropriate Graph or Plot

1. The tally chart shows the results of a survey about favourite snacks. Make a graph to compare the boys' and girls' favourites.

Snack	Boys	Girls
Potato chips	𝍷𝍷𝍷	𝍸 𝍸 𝍷𝍷
Popcorn	𝍸 𝍸 𝍷𝍷𝍷	𝍸
Corn chips	𝍸	𝍷𝍷𝍷𝍷

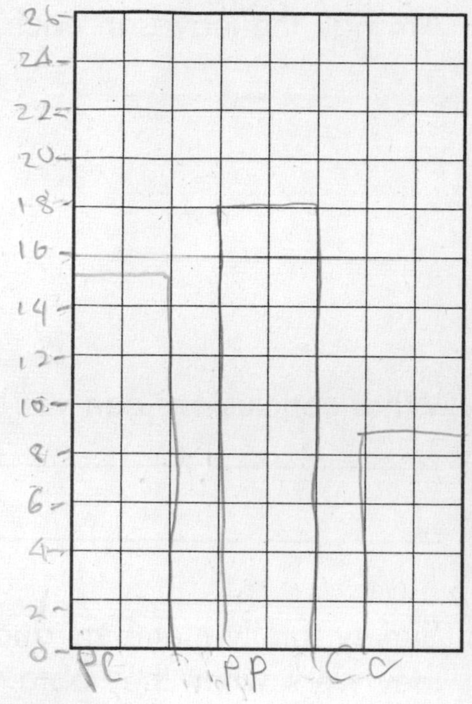

2. What conclusion can you draw from the graph?

pp (popcorn) is good.

3. Here are the ages of the senior citizens in the Scrabble Club: 68, 75, 81, 90, 67, 84, 73, 67, 68, 82, 75, 79, 86, 75, 69, 81, 75, 90, and 84. Make a plot to show the data.

4. What conclusion can you draw from your plot?

They are all old.

6/13

1. Use the data in the table to make the graph that will best show whether there is a relationship between height and mass for these six people.

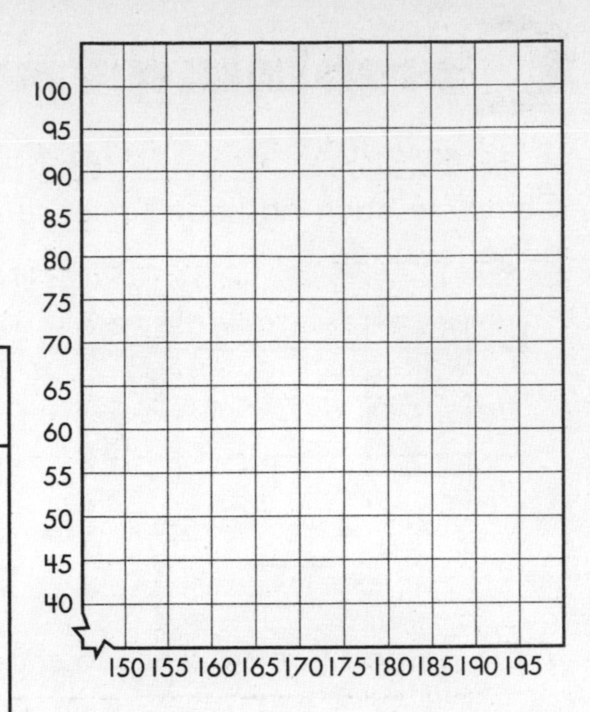

Name	Height (cm)	Mass (kg)
Dave	150	42
Chuy	170	64
Oliver	162	58
George	180	92
Ivor	161	63
Bob	198	98

2. What conclusion can you draw from your graph?

everyone is over 1 m.

3. The students in Mr. Fernando's class were asked to estimate how many drops of water can fit on a penny. Here are their estimates:
19, 16, 19, 30, 25, 19, 26, 18, 16, 25, 15, 17, 23, 25, 19, 20, 24, 26, 16, 17, 15, 25, 25, 20, and 15.
Make a plot to show the data.

4. What conclusion can you draw from your plot?

I think in most possible range is 12 - 25

FAMILY NOTE: Your child is learning that different kinds of graphs and plots are appropriate for displaying certain kinds of data. Help your child find examples of graphs in newspapers or magazines. Discuss together why each type of graph was selected to display the information.

Combining Fractions

Complete each addition sentence to show what fraction of the magazine page is shaded.

1. 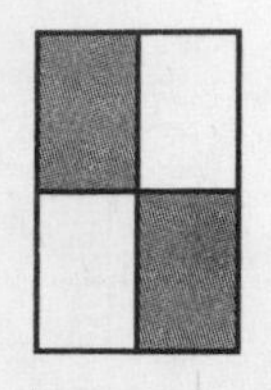

$\frac{1}{4} + \frac{1}{4} =$ ____

2. 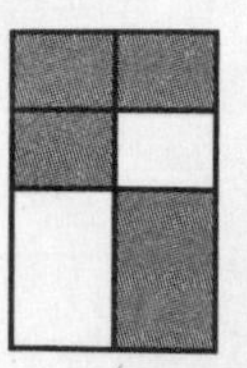

$\frac{3}{8} + \frac{1}{4} =$ ____

3. 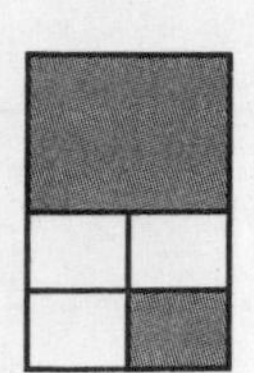

$\frac{1}{2} + \frac{1}{8} =$ ____

4. 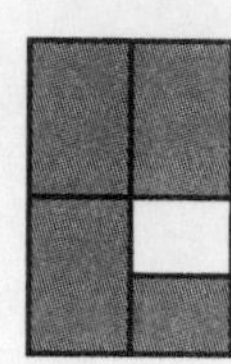

$\frac{3}{4} + \frac{1}{8} =$ ____

Write an addition sentence to show what fraction is shaded.

5. 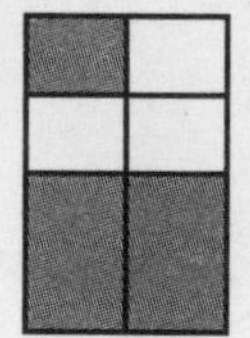

____

6. 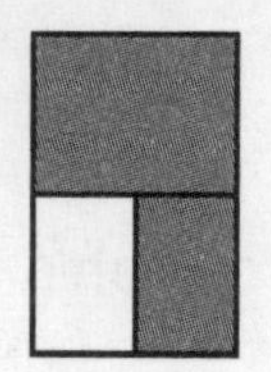

____

7. 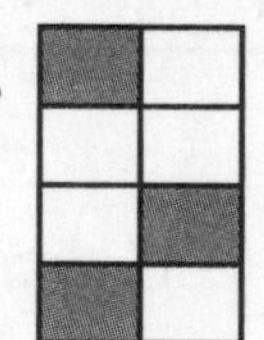

____

8. 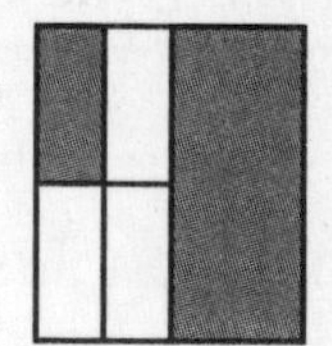

____

Write an addition sentence for each picture.
Write the sum as a mixed number.

9. 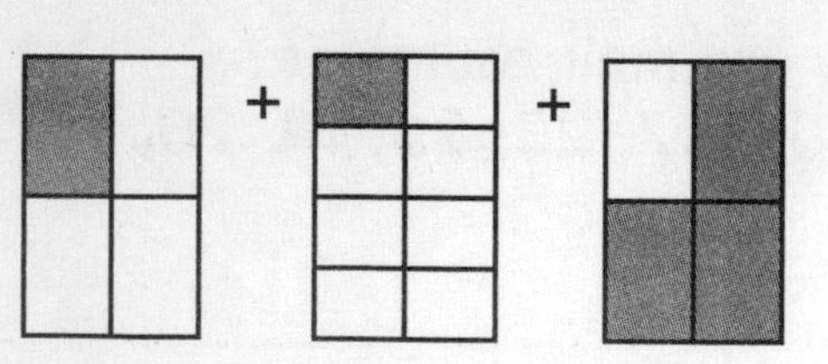

____

10. 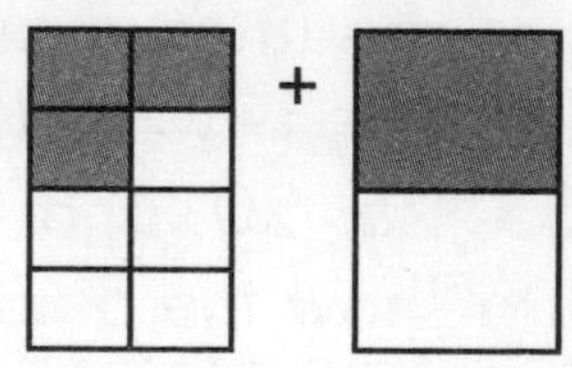

____

11. 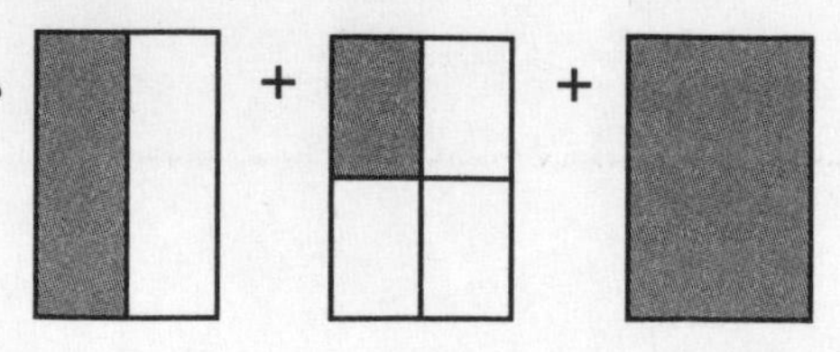

____

12. 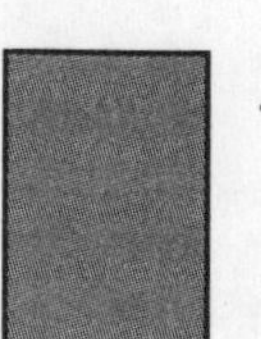 + 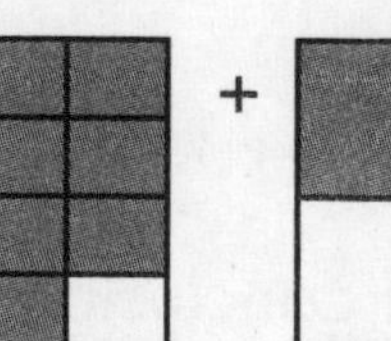

____

Add.

13. $\frac{3}{4} + \frac{3}{4} + 1\frac{1}{2} =$ ____ **14.** $\frac{1}{8} + \frac{1}{8} + \frac{1}{2} =$ ____ **15.** $2\frac{1}{4} + \frac{3}{4} + \frac{1}{2} =$ ____

Here are some magazine page layouts.
What fraction is represented by each section?

1. 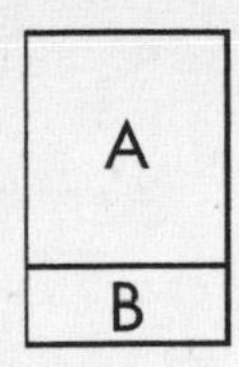

A ______

B ______

2. 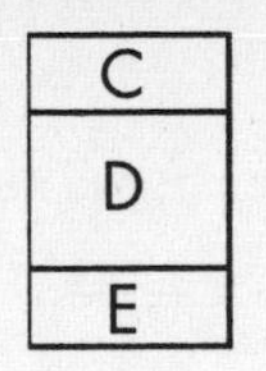

C ______

D ______

E ______

3. 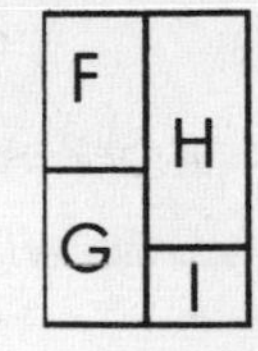

F ______

G ______

H ______

I ______

Write two equivalent fractions for each section.

4. A ___ ___ **5.** B ___ ___ **6.** C ___ ___ **7.** D ___ ___

Find the total amount of space for the following combined sections.
Show your work.
Write each sum as a fraction or a mixed number.

8. C + E ______________________________

9. A + D ______________________________

10. A + B + D ______________________________

11. C + E + H ______________________________

12. D + G + H ______________________________

13. A + A + D + G ______________________________

FAMILY NOTE: To add the fractions in Problems 8 to 13, your child may write equivalent fractions with the same denominator or use some other method. Ask your child to explain his or her methods to you.

Using Fractions and Decimals

Solve the problems in each set.
Show all your work.

1. a) How many 20 min videos could you watch in 60 min?

3

b) How many half-hour videos could you watch in 3 h?

6

c) How many 0.5 h videos could you watch in 2.5 h?

5

2. How many hours would it take to watch these videos?

a) six 2 h videos 12h

b) four 0.5 h videos 2.0h

c) three $\frac{3}{4}$ h videos 2.5h

3. How much longer is the first video than the second?

a) *Return of the Vampire*: 3 h *Going Home*: 1 h

2h

b) *Mr. Brown's Guest*: $2\frac{1}{2}$ h *Who, Me?*: $1\frac{1}{4}$ h

1.25s

c) *Elmer's Exercises*: 2.75 h *Road Race*: 0.5 h

270m

Solve the problems in each set.
Show all your work.

1. How much more do you need?

a) The recipe calls for 6 cups of rice. You have 4 cups.

2 ____________________

b) The recipe calls for 3 packages of marshmallows. You have $1\frac{1}{2}$ packages. $2\frac{3}{4}$ ____________________

c) The recipe calls for 2.5 kg of potatoes. You have 1.5 kg.

10 Kg ____________________

2. How many recipes can you make?

a) The recipe calls for 3 cups. You have 9 cups.

3 ____________________

b) The recipe calls for $\frac{1}{2}$ cup. You have $2\frac{1}{2}$ cups.

7 ____________________

c) The recipe calls for 0.75 kg. You have 3 kg.

25 ____________________

3. How many cans of punch will you have if the cans are the same size?

a) The recipe calls for 6 cans of juice and 3 cans of soda water.

2 ____________________

b) The recipe calls for $4\frac{1}{2}$ cans of juice and $2\frac{1}{2}$ cans of soda water.

5 ____________________

c) The recipe calls for 1.25 cans of juice and 1.25 cans of soda water.

0 ____________________

FAMILY NOTE: Although the three problems in each set are solved by using the same operation, each problem presents numbers in different forms (whole numbers, fractions, and decimals). These problem sets are designed to help your child see that operations with fractions and decimals are extensions of operations with whole numbers.

Adding and Subtracting Fractions and Mixed Numbers

Use your own procedures to find each sum.
Show all your work.

1. $\frac{1}{5} + \frac{3}{10} =$ ____________

2. $\frac{5}{8} + \frac{3}{4} =$ ____________

3. $\frac{1}{6} + \frac{2}{3} =$ ____________

4. $\frac{3}{8} + \frac{1}{2} =$ ____________

5. $\frac{2}{3} + \frac{2}{3} =$ ____________

6. $\frac{3}{10} + \frac{2}{5} =$ ____________

7. $\frac{7}{8} + \frac{1}{2} =$ ____________

8. $\frac{2}{3} + \frac{1}{6} =$ ____________

9. $\frac{1}{4} + \frac{3}{8} =$ ____________

10. $\frac{5}{6} + \frac{1}{3} =$ ____________

Use your own procedures to find each difference.
Show all your work.

11. $\frac{1}{4} - \frac{1}{8} =$ ____________

12. $\frac{7}{8} - \frac{3}{4} =$ ____________

13. $\frac{1}{2} - \frac{1}{4} =$ ____________

14. $\frac{1}{3} - \frac{1}{6} =$ ____________

15. $\frac{5}{6} - \frac{1}{3} =$ ____________

16. $\frac{3}{4} - \frac{1}{2} =$ ____________

17. $\frac{7}{10} - \frac{1}{2} =$ ____________

18. $\frac{3}{8} - \frac{1}{4} =$ ____________

19. $\frac{4}{5} - \frac{1}{10} =$ ____________

20. $\frac{2}{3} - \frac{1}{2} =$ ____________

Use your own procedures to find each sum.
Show all your work.

1. $1\frac{1}{4} + 3\frac{1}{8} =$ $4\frac{5}{8}$	**2.** $5\frac{1}{2} + \frac{3}{4} =$ $6\frac{1}{4}$
3. $2\frac{2}{3} + 3\frac{1}{6} =$ $5\frac{5}{6}$	**4.** $7\frac{1}{2} + 2\frac{1}{8} =$ $4\frac{5}{8}$
5. $1\frac{1}{6} + 2\frac{5}{6} =$ 4	**6.** $\frac{7}{10} + 4\frac{1}{5} =$ $4\frac{9}{10}$

Use your own procedures to find each difference.
Show all your work.

7. $4\frac{1}{3} - 2\frac{1}{6} =$ $2\frac{1}{6}$	**8.** $7\frac{1}{2} - 3\frac{3}{10} =$ $4\frac{1}{5}$
9. $7\frac{1}{2} - 4\frac{1}{4} =$ $3\frac{1}{4}$	**10.** $3\frac{7}{8} - \frac{1}{2} =$ $3\frac{3}{8}$
11. $6\frac{1}{4} - 1\frac{1}{8} =$ $1\frac{1}{8}$	**12.** $6\frac{1}{2} - 2\frac{1}{3} =$ $4\frac{1}{6}$

FAMILY NOTE: Your child is learning to add and subtract fractions and mixed numbers using his or her own procedures. Ask your child to explain how he or she completed a few of the problems on this page.

Operating with Decimals

1. Solve the problem.
Show all your work.

A goldsmith is going to make a gold chain 54 cm long. She will alternate links that are 1.5 cm and 0.75 cm in length. How many links of each size will she need?

Find each sum or difference.

2. 6.73 + 8.45	**3.** 1.84 + 7.96	**4.** 3.21 − 1.96	**5.** 16.24 + 12.32
6. 97.52 − 61.38	**7.** 5.378 + 2.457	**8.** 3.046 − 0.137	**9.** 8.514 − 1.329
10. 1.004 + 0.227	**11.** 0.358 + 6.148	**12.** 0.251 − 0.138	**13.** 6.222 + 3.459

Find each product.

1. 2.5×9

2. 6.2×5

3. 1.7×9

4. 4.3×4

5. 5.63×7

6. 8.46×4

7. 3.72×6

8. 6.41×5

9. 0.142×6

10. 1.305×4

11. 6.132×6

12. 5.395×2

Find each quotient. Show your work.

13. $9\overline{)6.3}$

14. $8\overline{)9.6}$

15. $6\overline{)8.4}$

16. $5\overline{)6.25}$

17. $4\overline{)1.24}$

18. $7\overline{)9.31}$

19. $2\overline{)3.58}$

20. $6\overline{)26.34}$

21. $5\overline{)10.65}$

22. $8\overline{)9.44}$

23. $3\overline{)2.88}$

24. $7\overline{)49.7}$

FAMILY NOTE: Ask your child to estimate each product or quotient before doing the paper-and-pencil work. This will help your child check the reasonableness of his or her solutions.

Calculating Percent

Write a fraction equivalent for each percent.

1. 10% ________ **2.** 50% ________ **3.** 1% ________

4. 25% ________ **5.** 75% ________ **6.** 20% ________

Use the fraction equivalent of each percent to mentally calculate the amount.

7. 25% of $40 ____________ **8.** 10% of $60 ____________

9. 75% of $12 ____________ **10.** 50% of $6.99 ____________

11. 20% of $49.98 ____________ **12.** 1% of $6 ____________

Complete each set of calculations.

13. 10% of $5 = ____________
1% of $5 = ____________
11% of $5 = ____________

14. 50% of $7.99 = ____________
10% of $7.99 = ____________
60% of $7.99 = ____________

15. 25% of $16 = ____________
10% of $16 = ____________
35% of $16 = ____________

16. 10% of $14 = ____________
5% of $14 = ____________
15% of $14 = ____________

Calculate.

17. 50% of $25 ____________ **18.** 10% of $13 ____________

19. 15% of $30 ____________ **20.** 60% of $30 ____________

21. 11% of $50 ____________ **22.** 75% of $200 ____________

23. 35% of $60 ____________ **24.** 25% of $25 ____________

Complete the chart to find the sale price of each item.
For Problem 6, use a sale item you found advertised in a newspaper or catalogue.

Original Price	Percent Off	Amount Off ($)	Sale Price ($)
1.  $79.99	10%		
2. 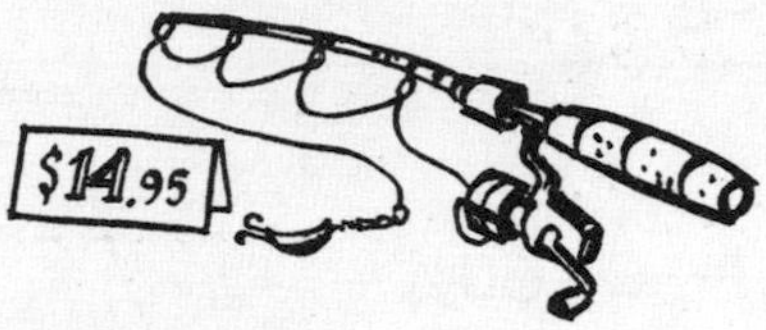 $14.95	15%		
3.  $199.95	50%		
4.  $25.00	25%		
5.  $60.00	75%		
6. Choose your own.			

FAMILY NOTE: Your child is learning to find a percent of a given amount of money. She or he may use a fraction or decimal equivalent, or apply some other strategy for calculating percent. Ask your child to explain his or her methods.

Using Percents to Compare Data

Two hundred people were surveyed about their eye colour.
The results are shown on the circle graph.
Tell how many people said they have each eye colour.

1. blue: ____________

2. brown: __________

3. green: ___________

4. grey: ____________

5. hazel: ___________

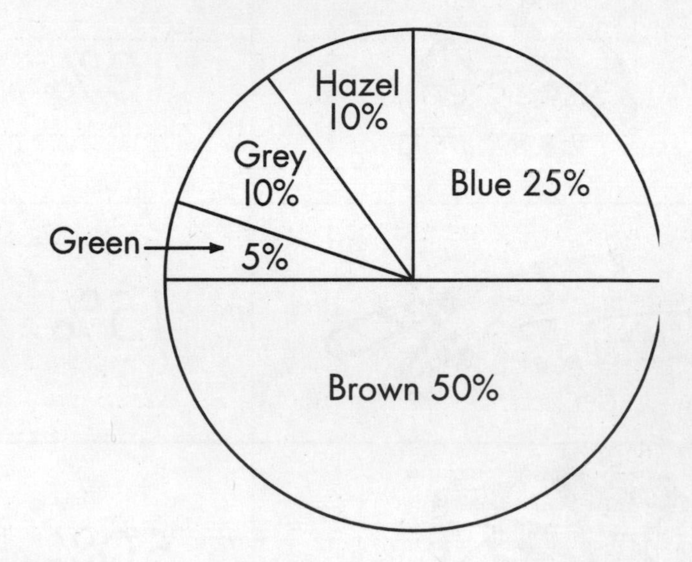

Five hundred people were surveyed about their favourite fairy tale characters. The results are shown on the circle graph.
Tell how many people named each character.

6. Snow White: __________

7. Rapunzel: _____________

8. Rumpelstiltskin: ________

9. Little Red Riding Hood: _____________

10. Cinderella: ___________

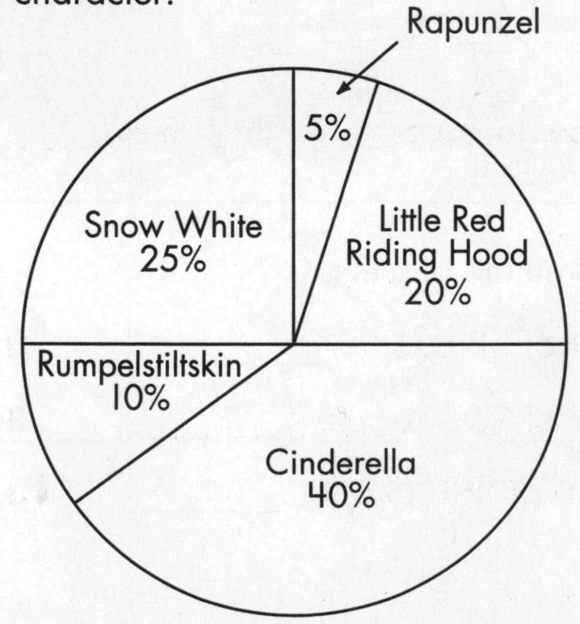

11. What three characters combined make up the same percent as Cinderella? ______________________________

____

1. Survey a total of 20 friends and family members. Ask which flavour of ice cream each prefers: vanilla, chocolate, or strawberry. Record their responses on the tally chart.

Vanilla	
Chocolate	
Strawberry	

2. Calculate the percent of people who chose each flavour.

Vanilla: ______________

Chocolate: ___________

Strawberry: __________

In a recent survey of 300 sports fans, 40% said they prefer afternoon games and 60% said they prefer night games.

3. How many people prefer afternoon games? ________________________

4. How many prefer night games? ___________________________________

Calculate the percent.

5. 24 of 48 people ________

6. 150 of 600 people ________

7. 25 of 250 people ________

8. 40 of 160 people ________

9. 100 of 400 people ________

10. 30 of 150 people ________

FAMILY NOTE: Your child is learning to use percents to compare data. The work on this page reinforces an understanding that the total number in a percent problem does not need to be 100.

Identifying Angles

Name each angle as acute, right, obtuse, straight, or reflex.

1.

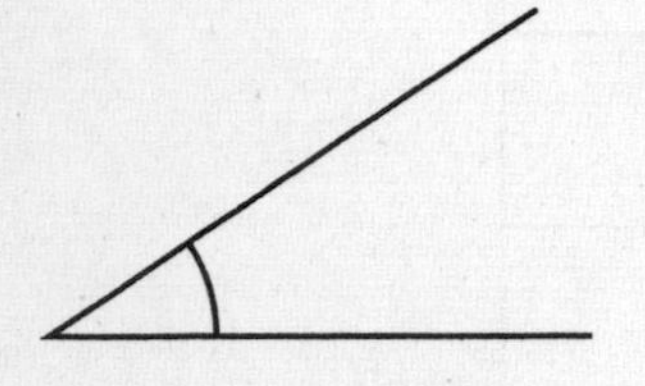

acute

2.

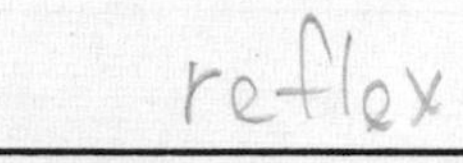

reflex

3.

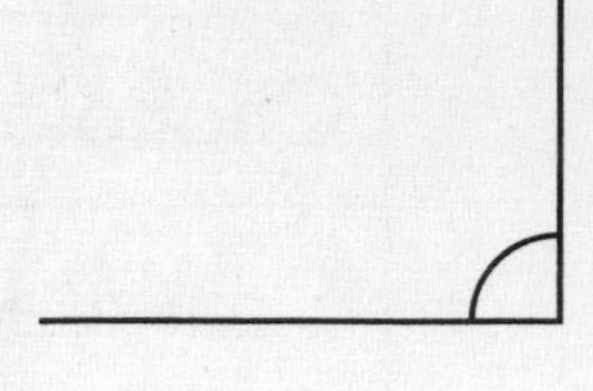

right

4.

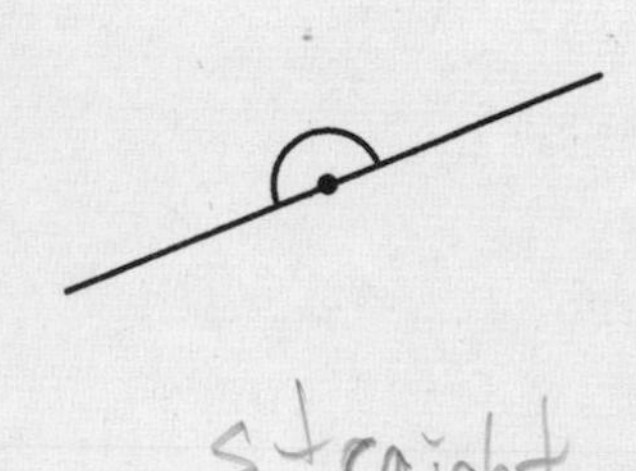

straight

5.

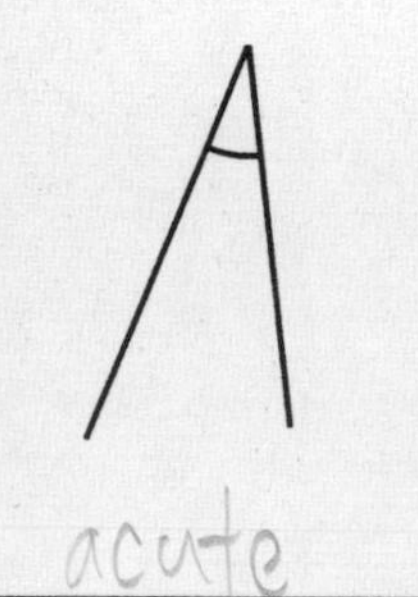

acute

6.

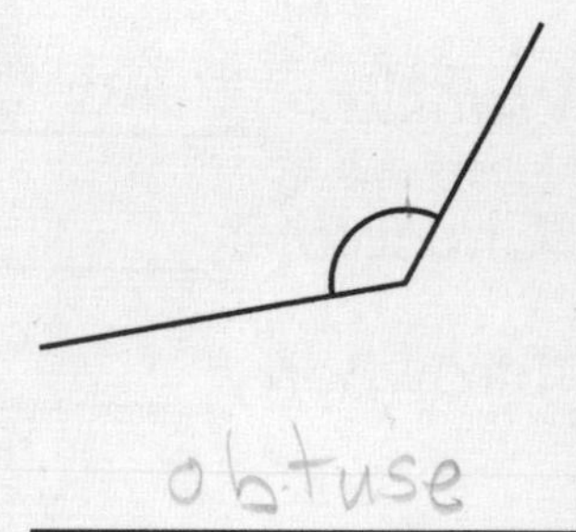

obtuse

7.

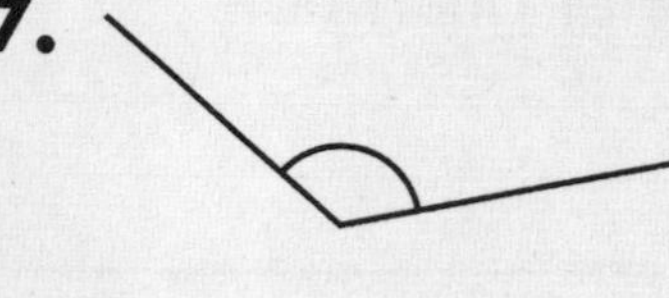

obtuse

8.

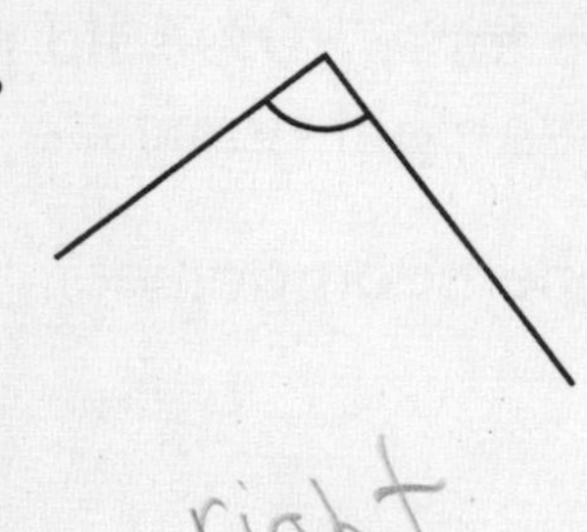

right

9.

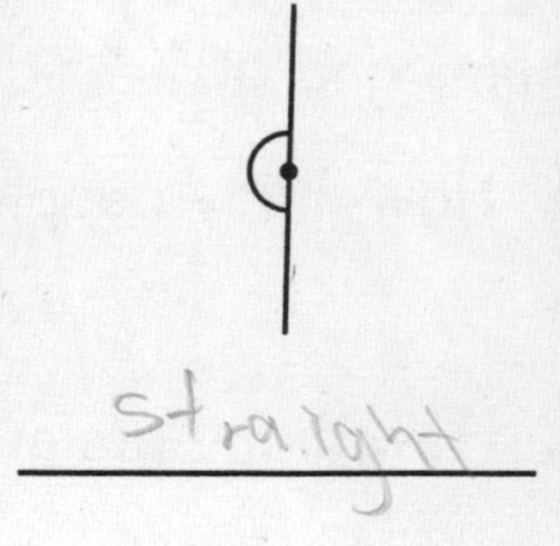

straight

Draw an example of each kind of angle.

10.

reflex

11.

acute

12.

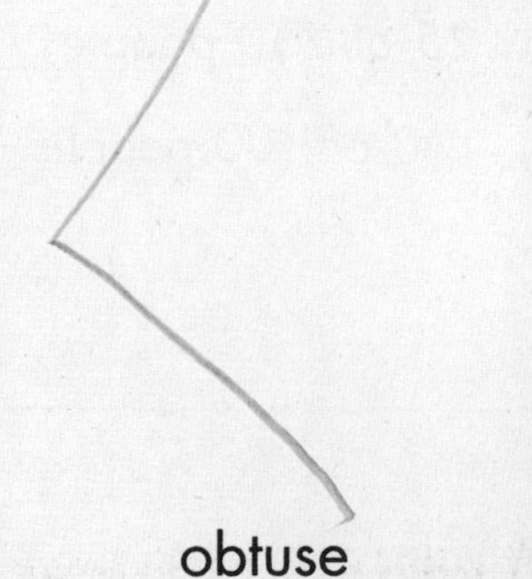

obtuse

Look around your home or neighbourhood.
Find two or three examples of each kind of angle.
Draw and label a picture of each example you find.

acute 	right 
obtuse 	reflex 

FAMILY NOTE: Your child is learning to identify types of angles in the environment through visual inspection. Help him or her find examples of each type of angle. For example, the hands of the clock at 9:00 make a right angle (90°) and a reflex angle (greater than 180°).

Finding Angle Measures Using Power Polygons

Each of these figures is made with identical Power Polygons that meet at a centre point. Write the measure of each angle that touches the centre point.

1.

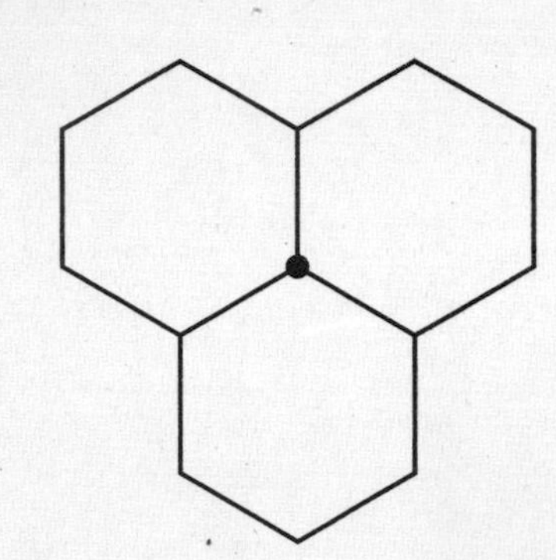

____

2.

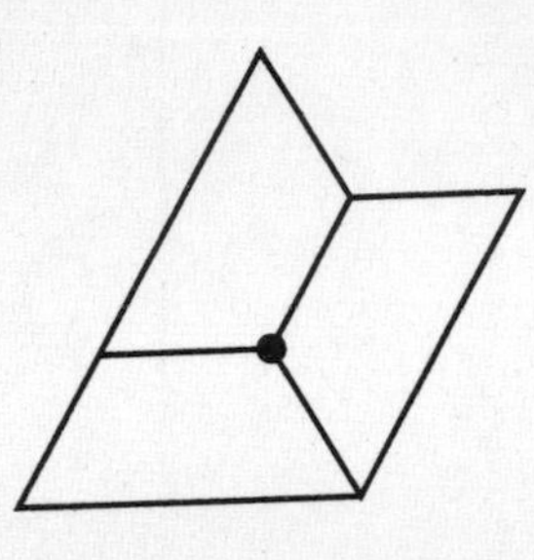

____

3.

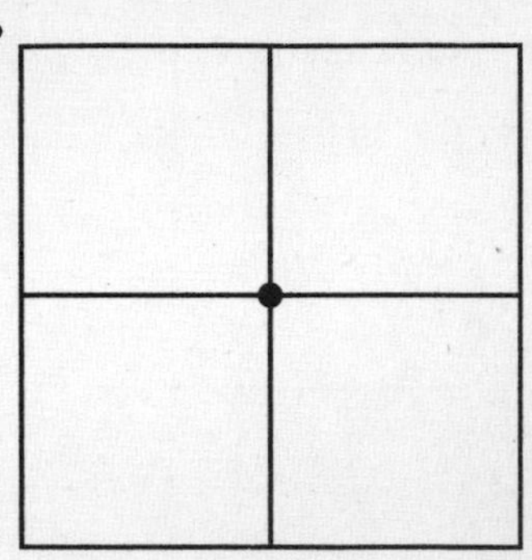

____

4.

____

5.

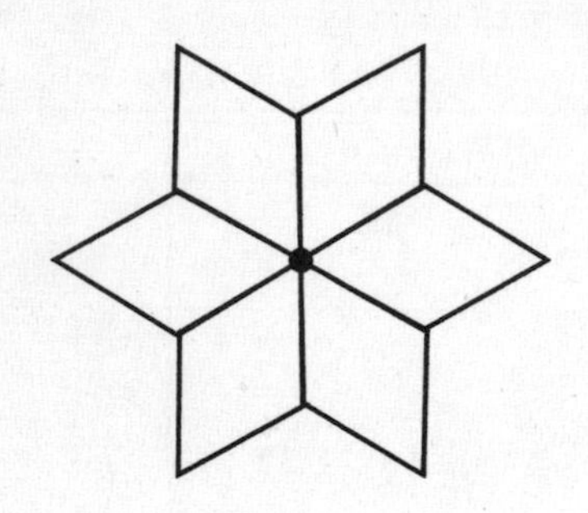

____

6.

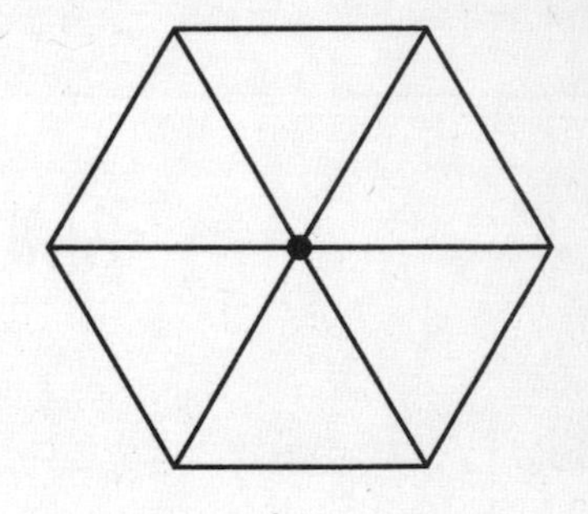

____

7.

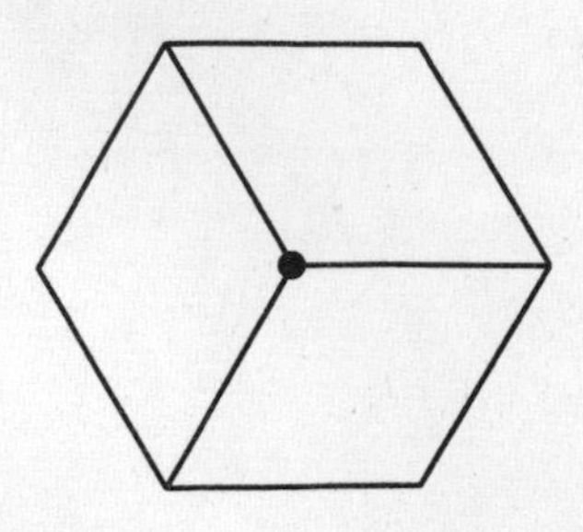

____

8.

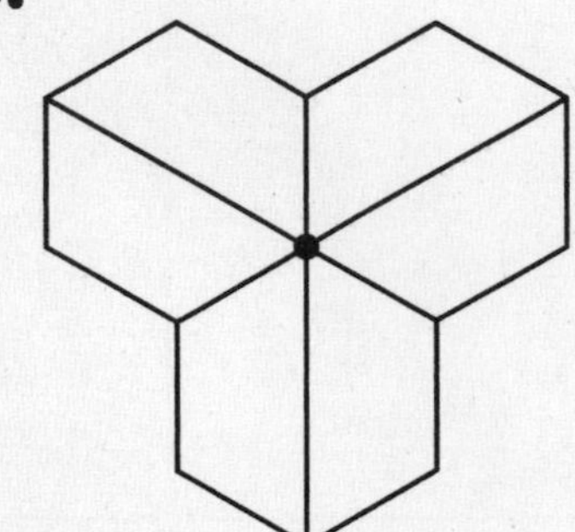

____

9.

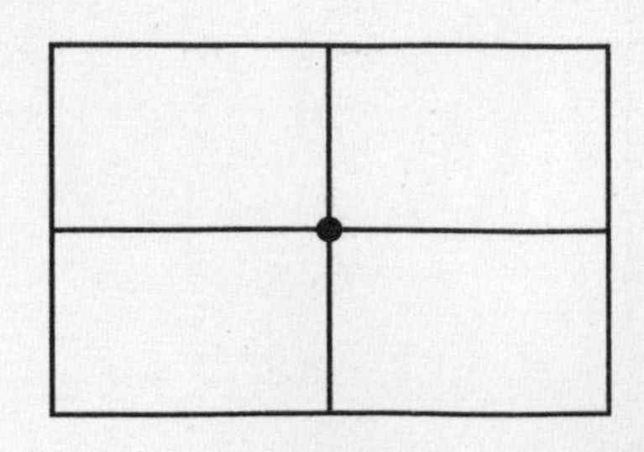

____

1. Each of these figures is made with Power Polygons. Write the measure of each marked angle.

a)

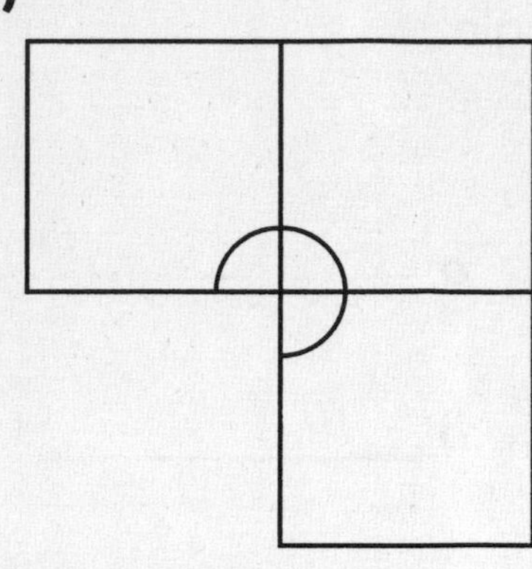

____

b)

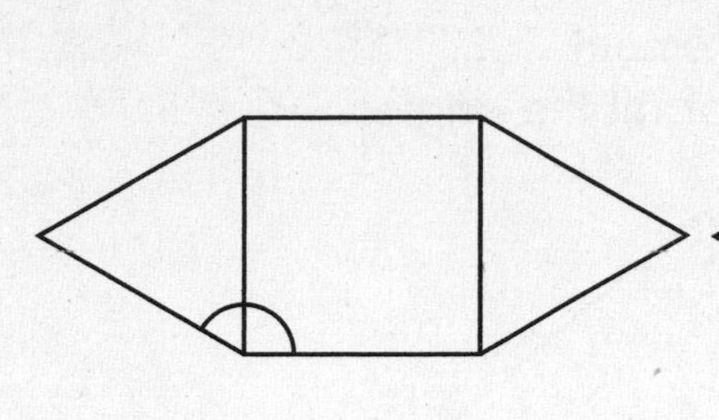

____

c)

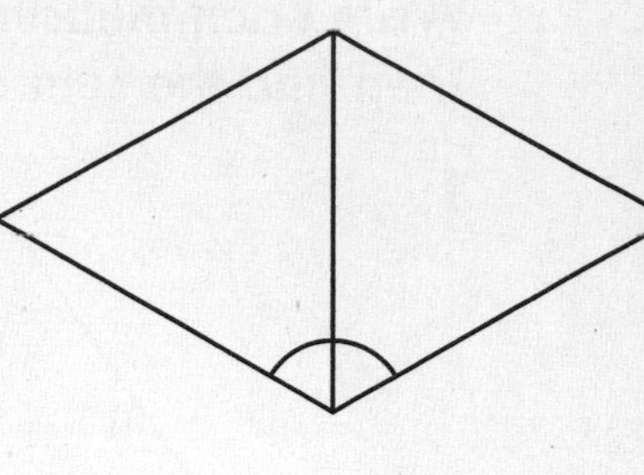

____

d)

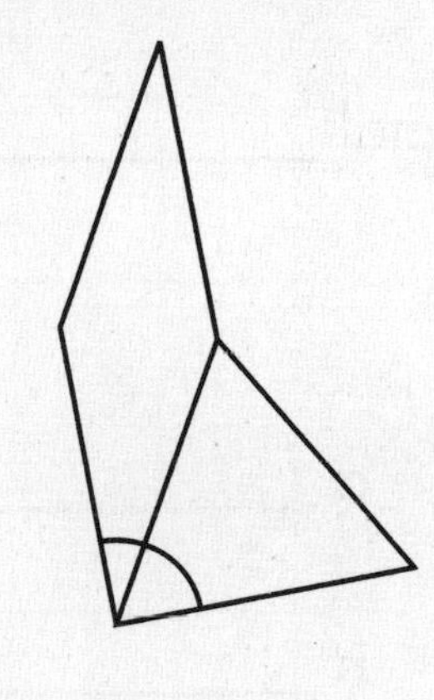

____

e)

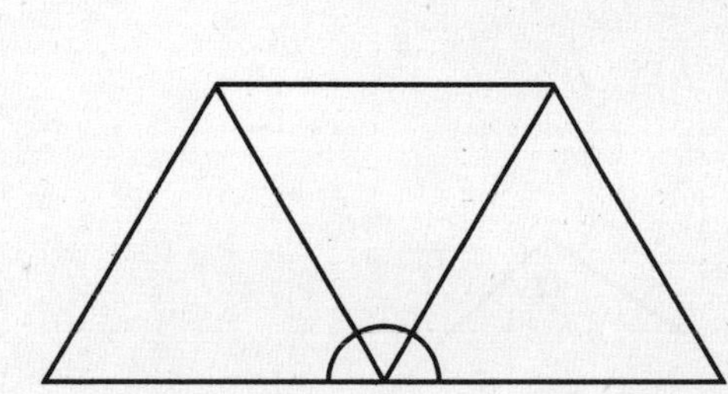

____

f)

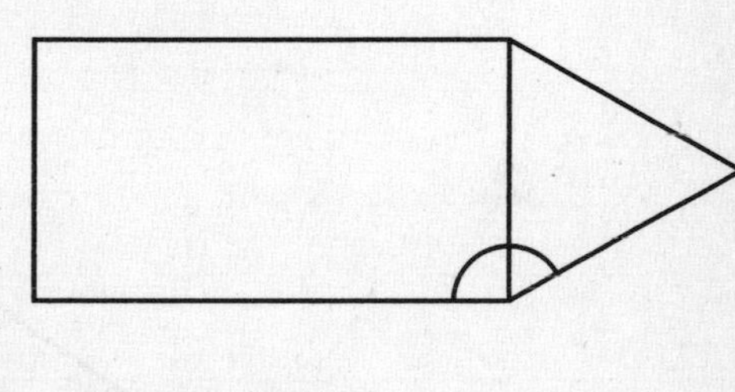

____

2. Name each angle from Problem 1 as acute, right, obtuse, straight, or reflex.

a) __________ **b)** __________

c) __________ **d)** __________

e) __________ **f)** __________

FAMILY NOTE: Your child has been exploring the angle measures of Power Polygons (models of various 2-D figures), using the fact that a full rotation measures 360°. In the next few days, your child will be learning to measure angles using a protractor.

Using a Protractor

Use a protractor to measure the angles in each triangle.
Write each measurement.
Then find the sum of all the angles.

1.

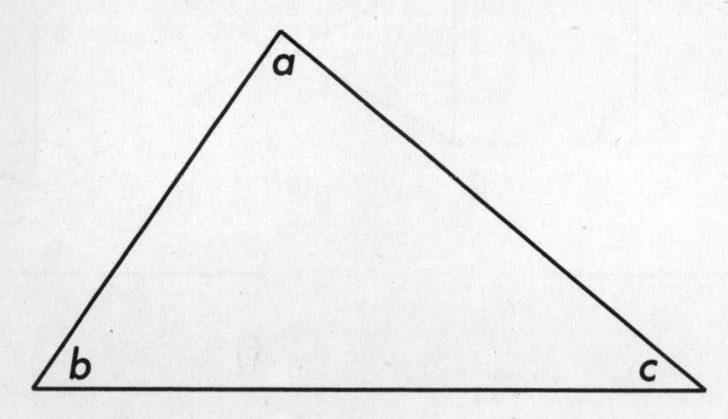

a ____________

b ____________

c ____________

Total ____________

2.

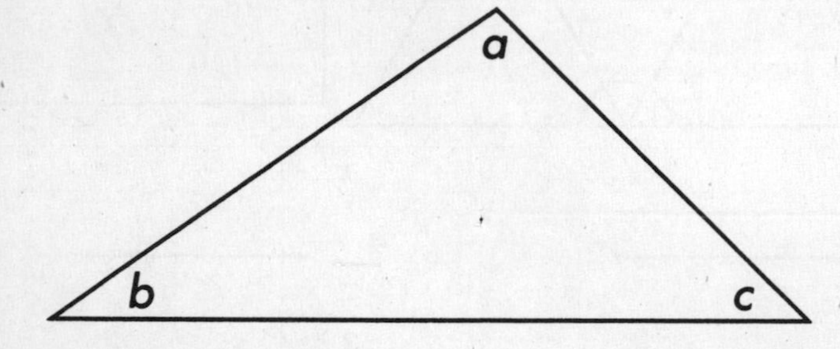

a ____________

b ____________

c ____________

Total ____________

3.

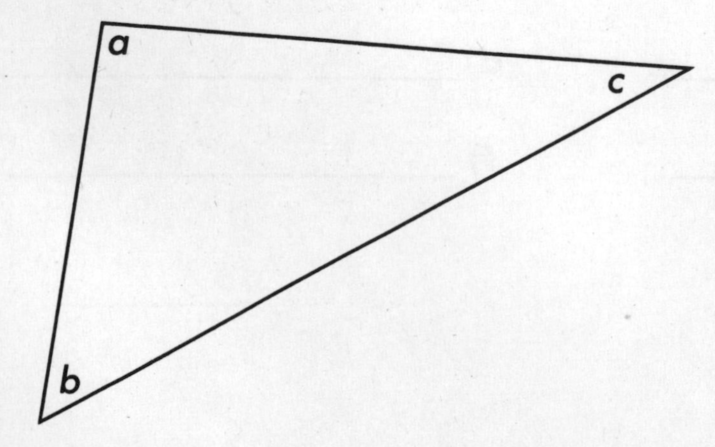

a ____________

b ____________

c ____________

Total ____________

Use a protractor to measure each angle.

1.

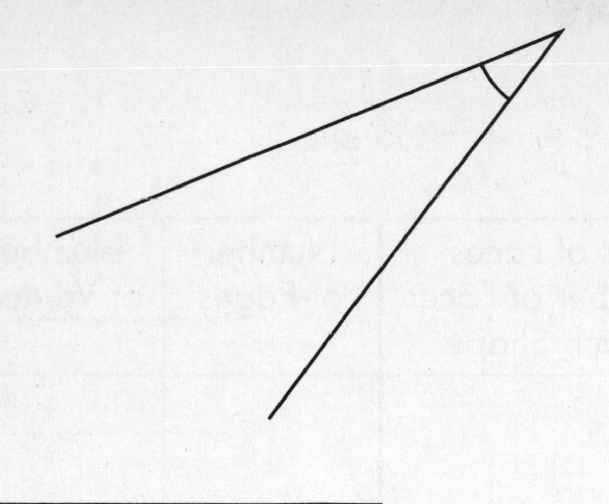

____

2.

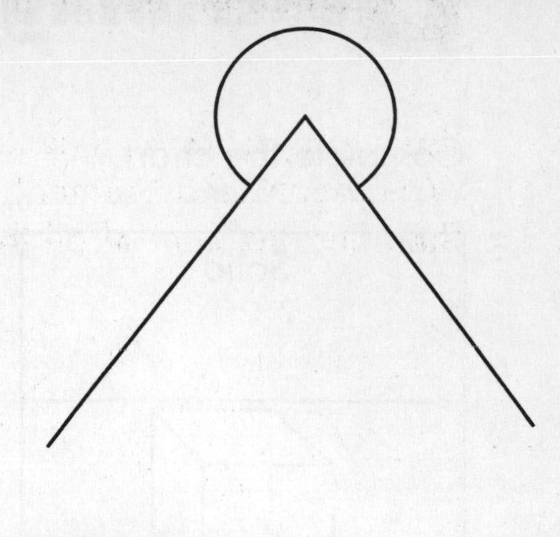

____

3.

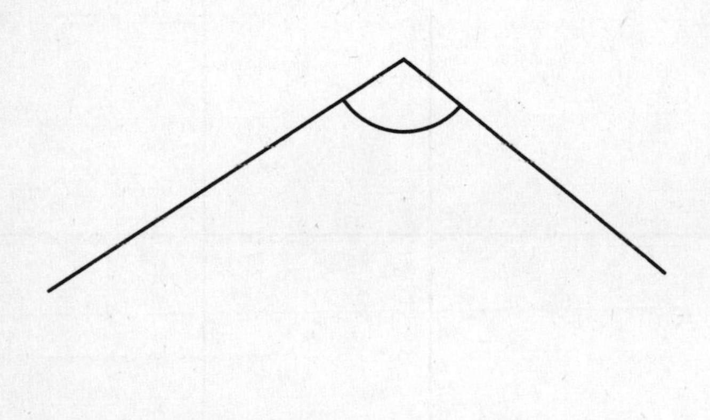

____

4.

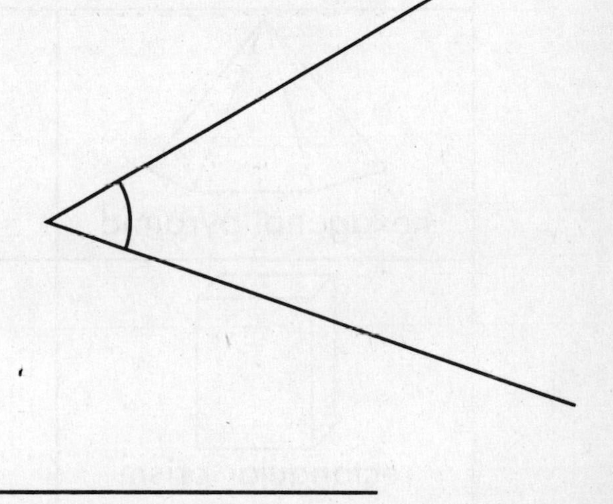

____

Draw each type of angle, then measure it.

5. an acute angle

____

6. an obtuse angle

____

FAMILY NOTE: Your child is learning to use a protractor to measure and draw angles. Please check to make sure your child understands how to use the scales on the protractor.

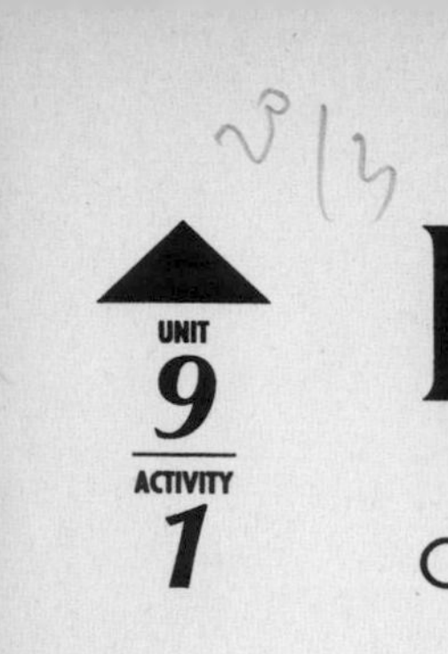

Describing Solids

Complete the chart.

Solid	Shapes of Faces and Number of Faces with Each Shape	Number of Edges	Number of Vertices
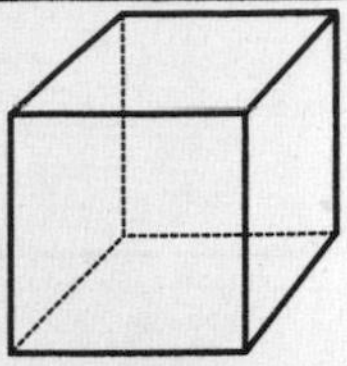 cube			
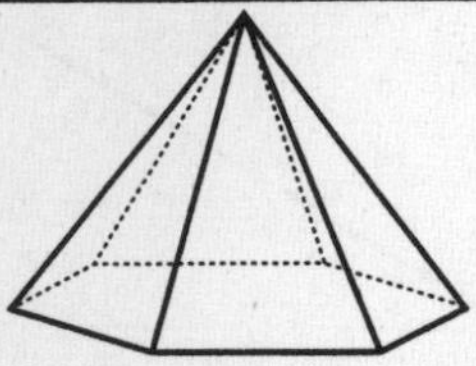 hexagonal pyramid			
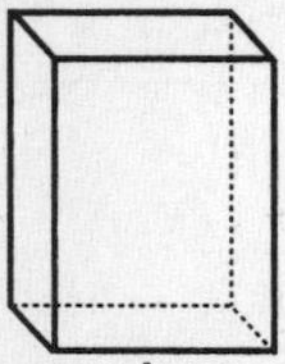 rectangular prism			
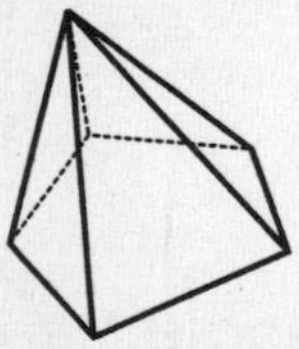 pentagonal pyramid			
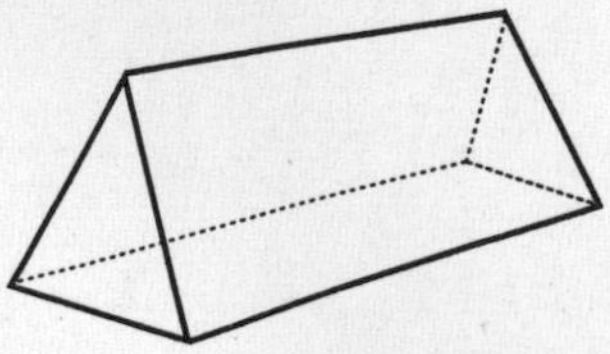 triangular prism			
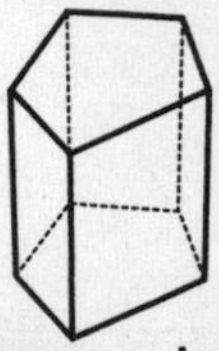 pentagonal prism			

Write the name of the solid you could make from each net.

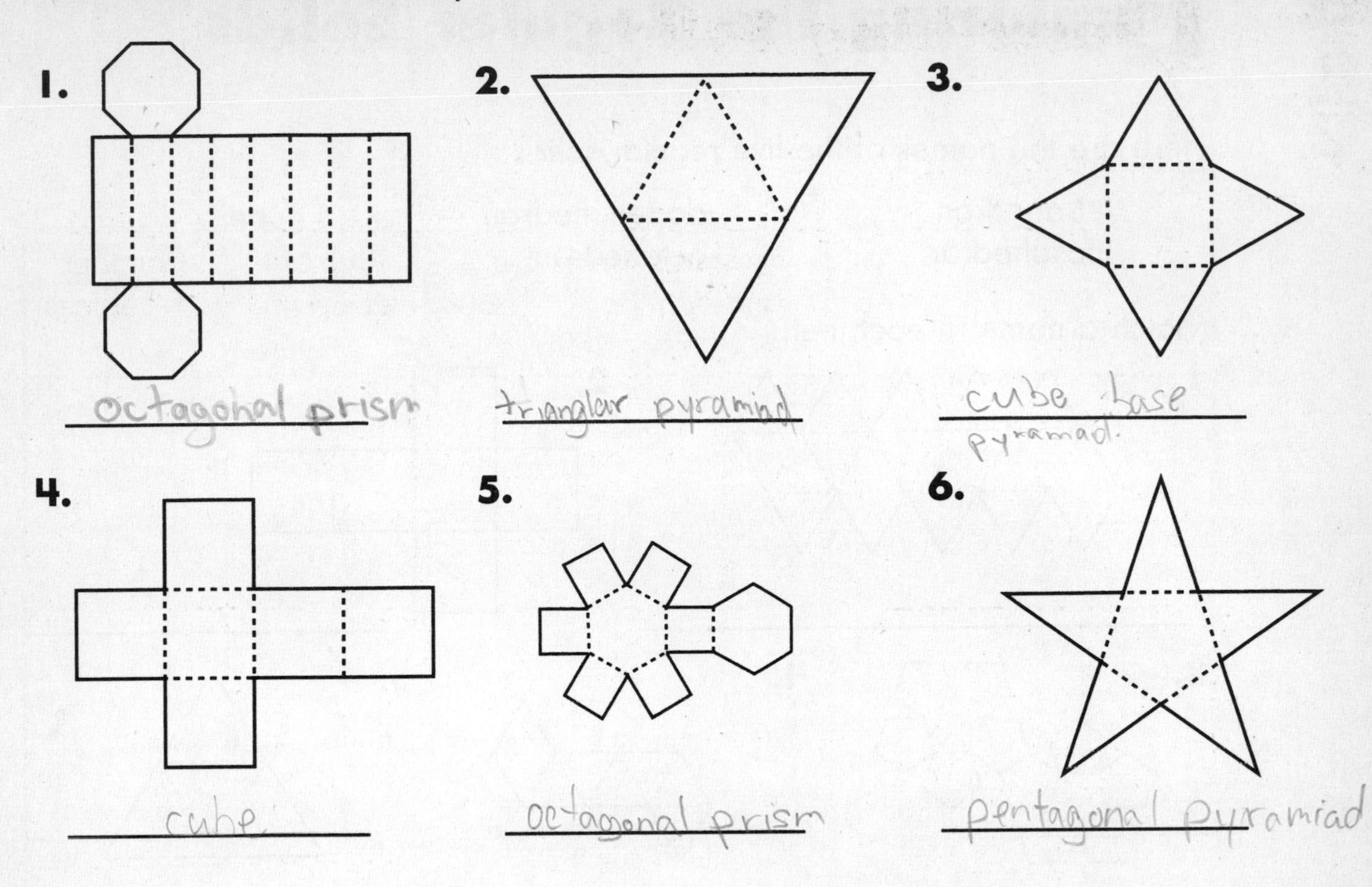

Circle each net that could be folded into a cube.

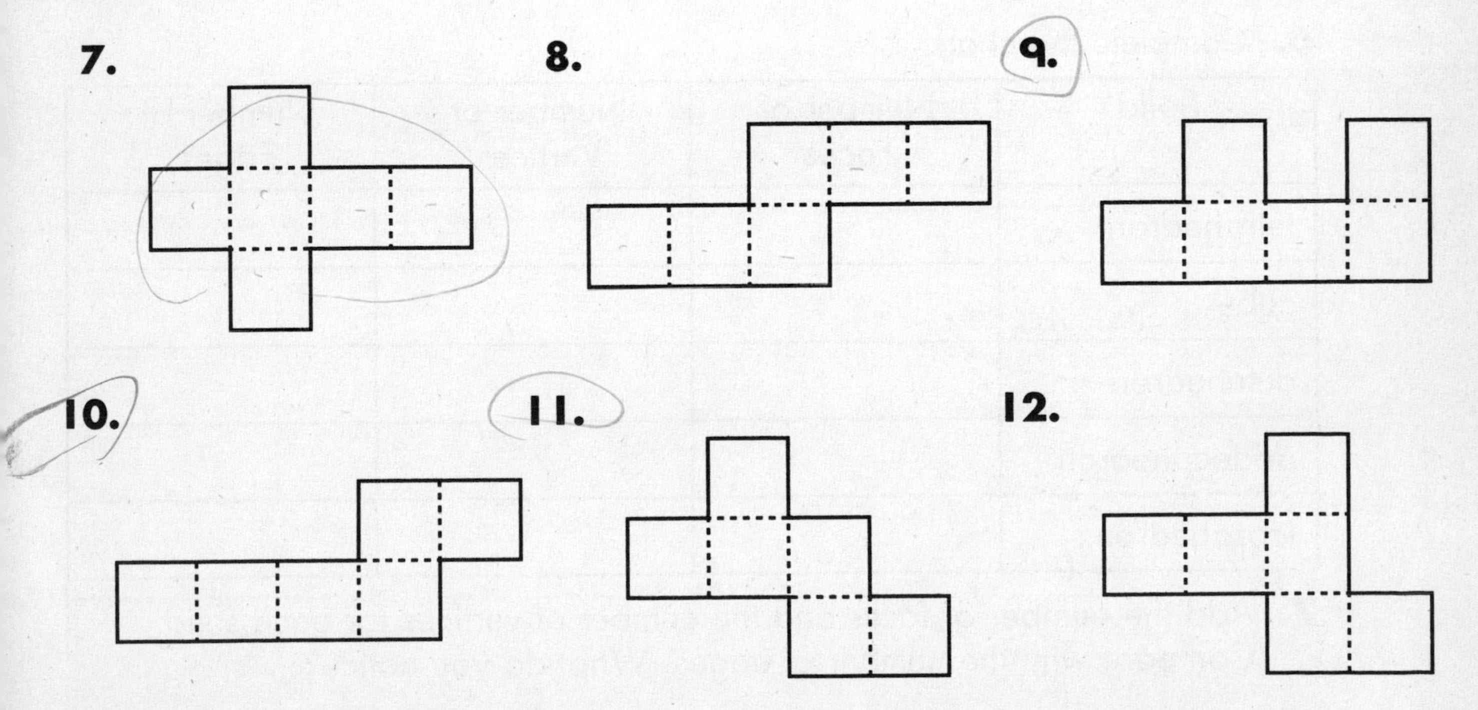

FAMILY NOTE: Your child has been building, analyzing, and describing geometric solids. She or he is learning to identify various pyramids and prisms from their nets. For Problems 7 to 12, your child could check his or her predictions by tracing each net, cutting it out, and folding to see if it can form a cube.

Exploring the Regular Solids

Here are the names of the five regular solids.

tetrahedron icosahedron dodecahedron octahedron cube

Match a name to each net.

1.

Octahedron

2.

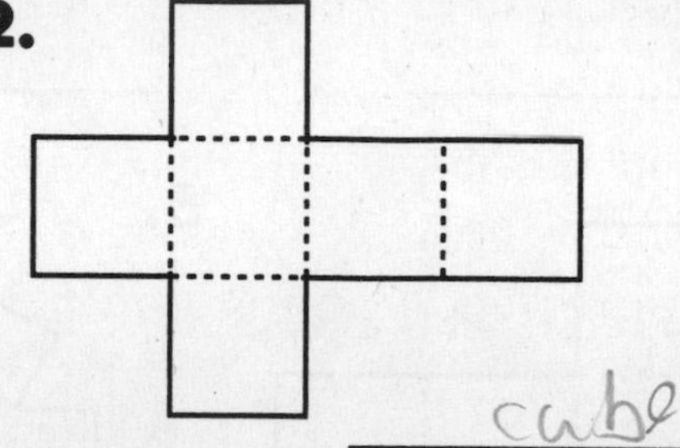

cube

3.

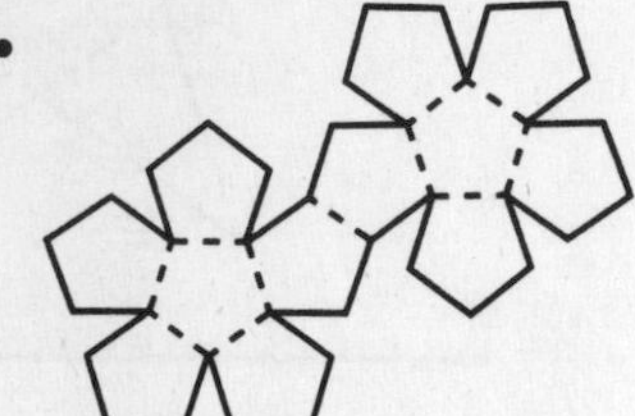

dodecahedron

4.

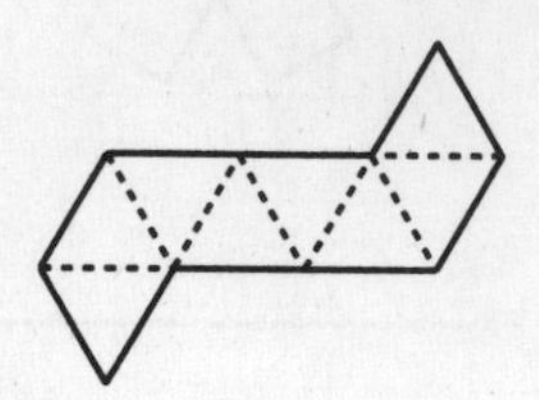

tetrahedron

5.

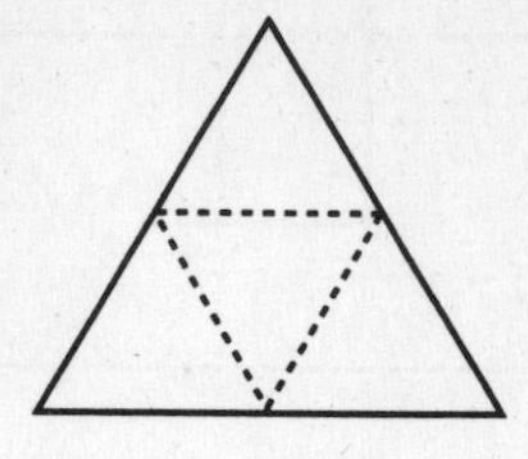

Icosahedron

6. Complete the chart.

Solid	Number of Faces	Number of Vertices	Number of Edges
tetrahedron	5		
cube	6		
octahedron	8		
dodecahedron	12		
icosahedron	20		

7. Add the number of faces and the number of vertices for each solid. Compare with the number of edges. What do you notice?

____

____

20/3

Here are the five regular solids.

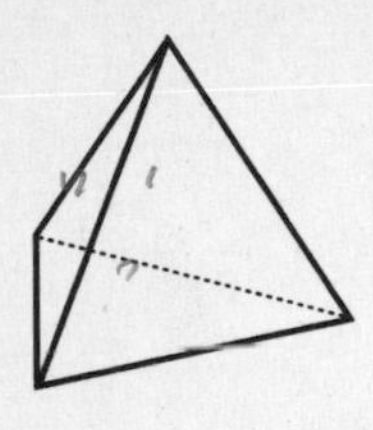
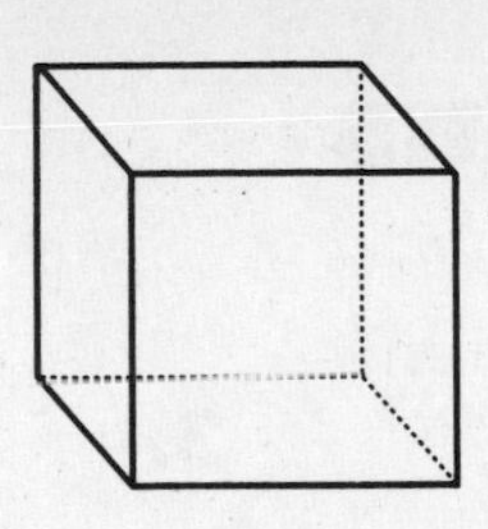
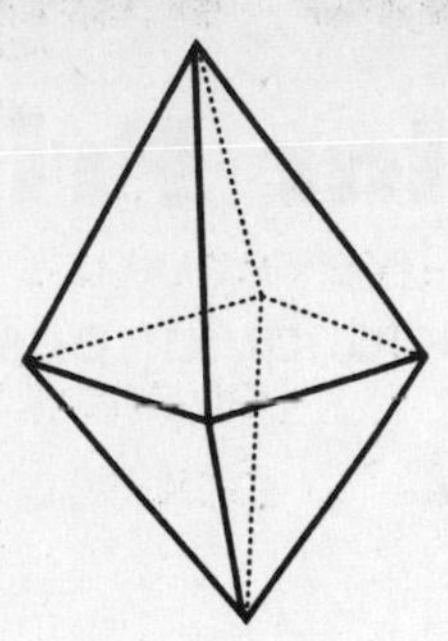
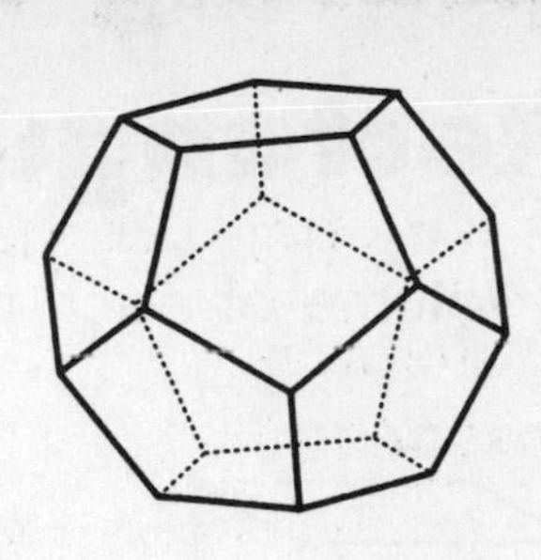
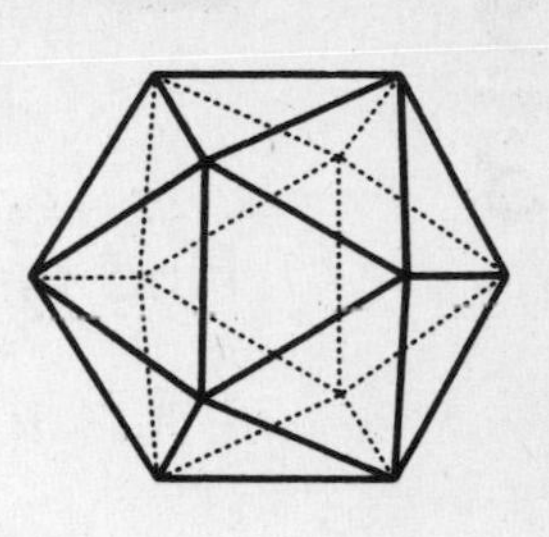

tetrahedron cube octahedron dodecahedron icosahedron

Name the regular polygon that forms the faces of each regular solid.

1. tetrahedron ______________________
2. cube ______________________
3. octahedron ______________________
4. dodecahedron ______________________
5. icosahedron ______________________

6. The cube is sometimes called a hexahedron.
Why do you think this is so?

____

____

7. Which of the regular solids looks like two square pyramids attached at their bases? ______________________

FAMILY NOTE: Your child has been investigating the five regular solids identified over 2000 years ago by Greek mathematicians. He or she has learned that the five regular solids are built from squares, equilateral triangles, or regular pentagons.

Doubling the Volumes of Rectangular Prisms

Find the volume of each rectangular prism.

1.

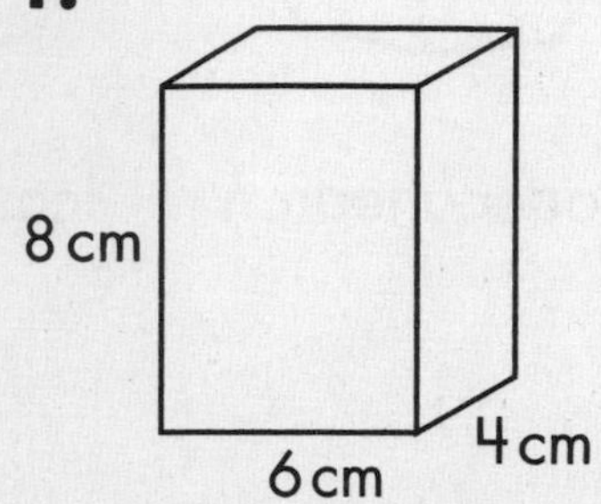

Volume = ______ cm^3

2.

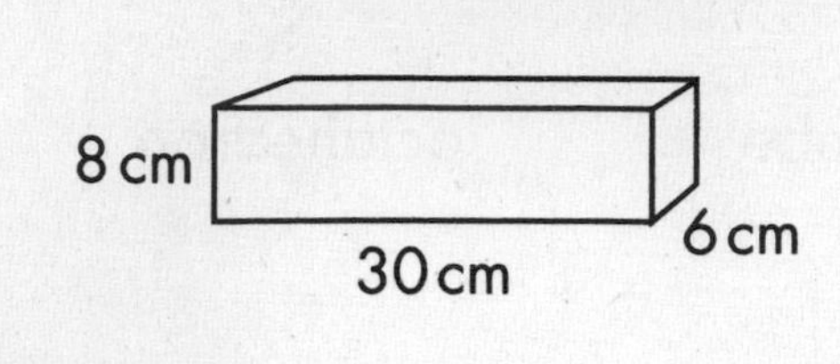

Volume = ______ cm^3

3.

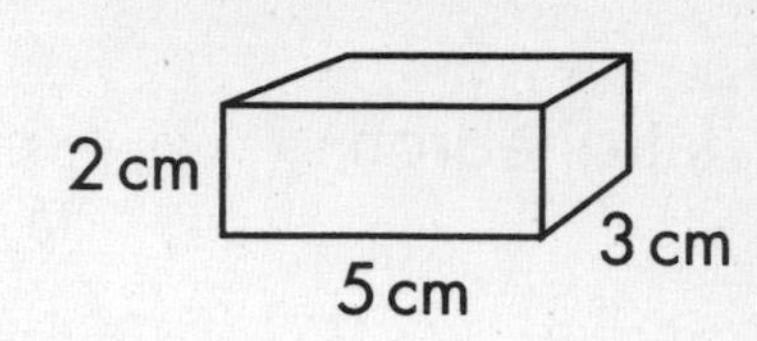

Volume = ______ cm^3

Sketch a rectangular prism with double the volume for each of the following. Label the dimensions.

4.

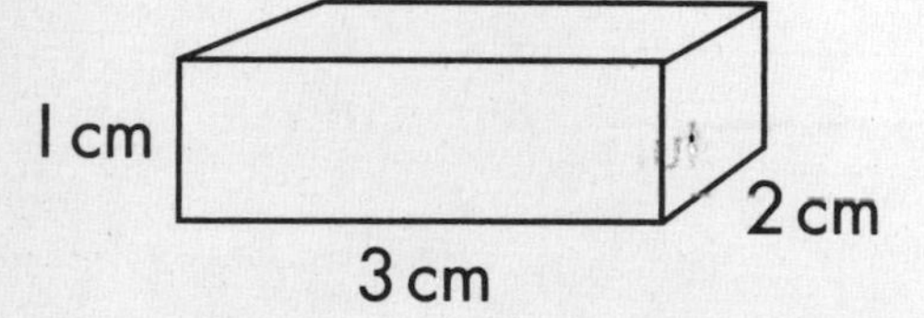

Volume = ______ cm^3 Volume = ______ cm^3

5.

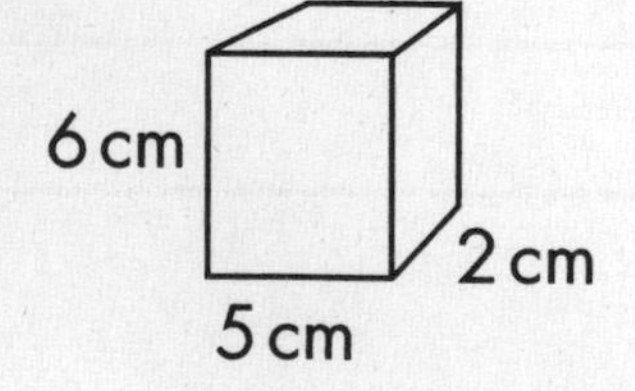

Volume = ______ cm^3 Volume = ______ cm^3

6.

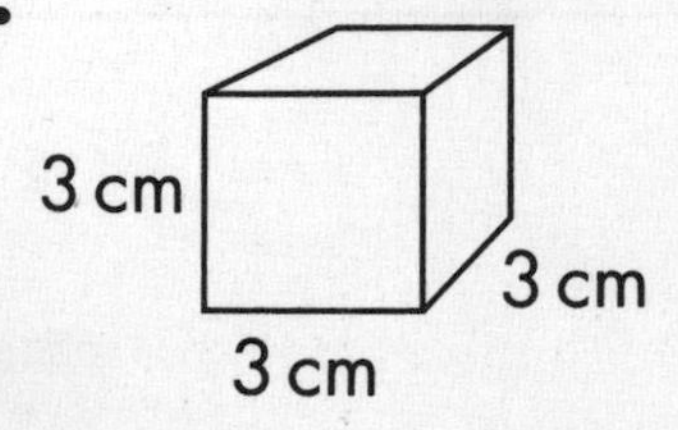

Volume = ______ cm^3 Volume = ______ cm^3

Sketch a rectangular prism for each volume.
Label the dimensions.

1. Volume = 12 cm^3	**2.** Volume = 24 cm^3
3. Volume = 16 cm^3	**4.** Volume = 32 cm^3

5. Sketch as many rectangular prisms as you can with double the volume of the one below. Label the dimensions.

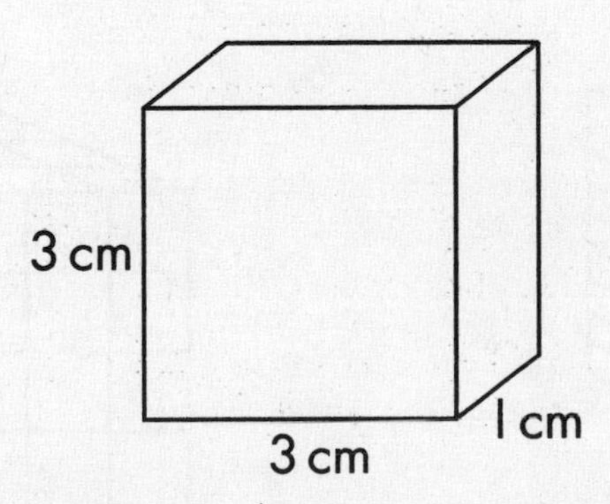

FAMILY NOTE: Your child has learned the formula *Volume* = *length* × *width* × *height* for finding the volume of a rectangular prism. He or she has been exploring the relationship between changes to the side lengths and changes in volume.

Relating Volume and Surface Area

Each rectangular prism is made of centimetre cubes.
Find the volume and surface area of each prism.

1.

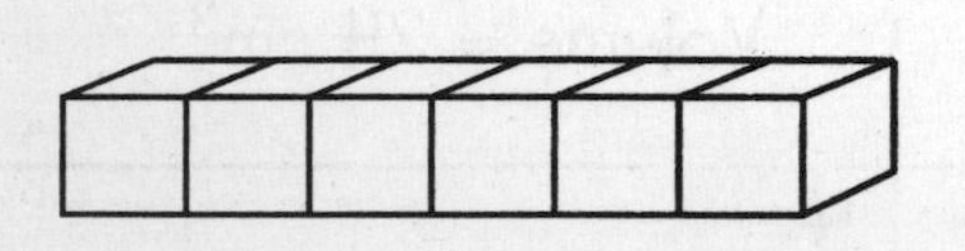

Volume: ____________________

Surface area: ______________

2.

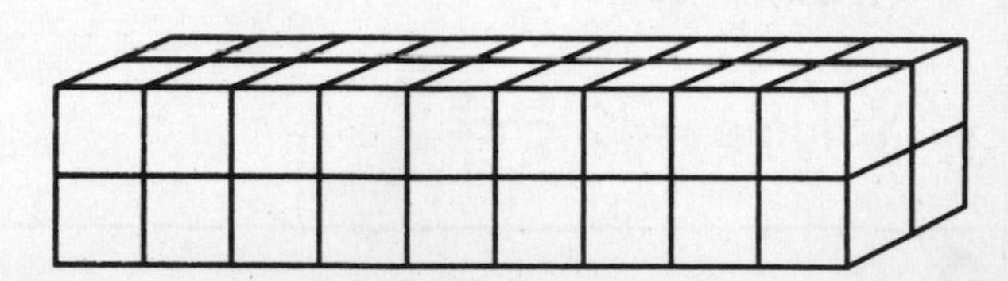

Volume: ____________________

Surface area: ______________

3.

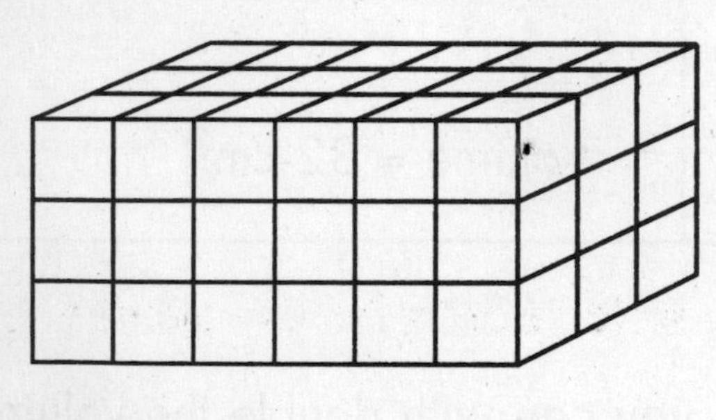

Volume: ____________________

Surface area: ______________

4.

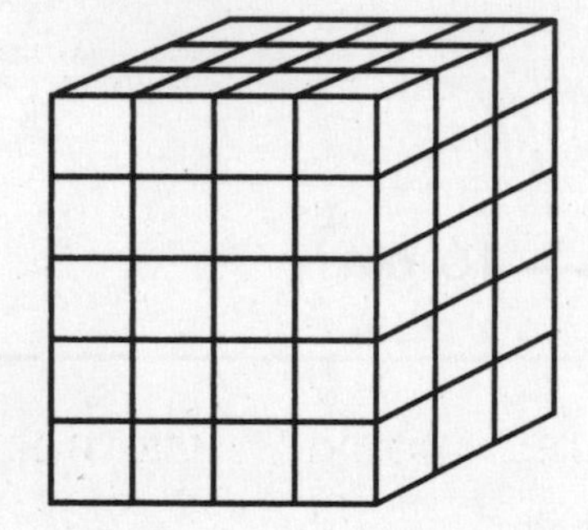

Volume: ____________________

Surface area: ______________

5.

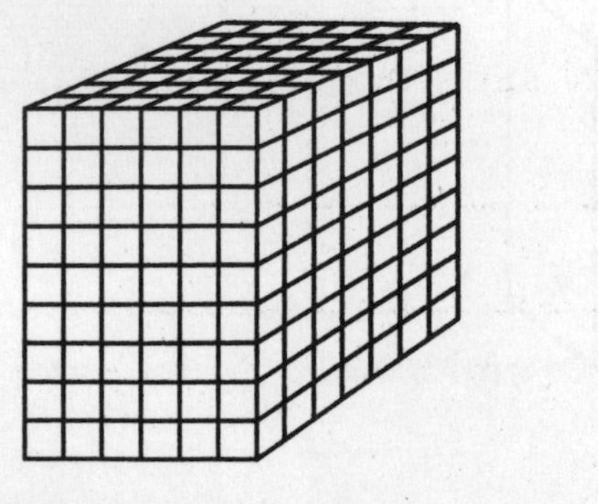

Volume: ____________________

Surface area: ______________

6.

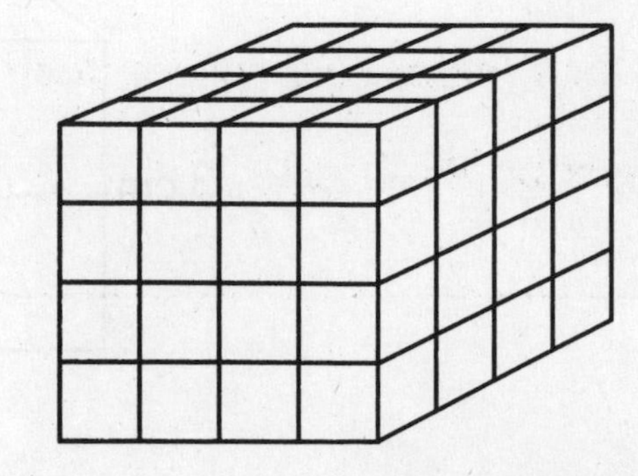

Volume: ____________________

Surface area: ______________

Each rectangular prism was made with 16 centimetre cubes.
Write the dimensions of each prism.
Then find each surface area.

1.

Dimensions: ____________________

Surface area: ____________________

2.

Dimensions: ____________________

Surface area: ____________________

3.

Dimensions: ____________________

Surface area: ____________________

4.

Dimensions: ____________________

Surface area: ____________________

5. What is the volume of each rectangular prism above? ____________________

6. Which rectangular prism has the least surface area for its volume? __________

Describe its shape. ____

____

7. Which rectangular prism has the greatest surface area for its volume? __________

Describe its shape. ____

____

FAMILY NOTE: Your child has been exploring the relationship between volume and surface area. Examine some food packages, such as cereal or cracker boxes, with your child. Ask: "What other box dimensions could the company have used for this package if they had wanted to keep the same volume?" and "Why do you think they chose these side lengths instead of different ones?"

Determining Experimental Probability

Each tally chart shows the results of an experiment.
Express the probability of each outcome as a fraction.

1.

Coin Tossing	
heads	𝍸 𝍸 𝍸 𝍸 𝍸 |
tails	𝍸 𝍸 𝍸 𝍸 𝍸 𝍸 ||||

Total number of tosses: ____
Probability of coin landing:

heads up ________

tails up ________

2.

Paper Cup Tossing	
on its side	𝍸 𝍸 𝍸 𝍸 𝍸 |
on its top	𝍸 𝍸 |
on its bottom	|||

Total number of tosses: ____
Probability of cup landing:

on its side ________

on its top ________

on its bottom ________

3.

Folded Paper Tossing	
fold down	𝍸 𝍸 𝍸 𝍸 𝍸
fold up	𝍸 𝍸 𝍸 𝍸 |||
on an end	||

Total number of tosses: ____
Probability of paper landing:

fold down ________

fold up ________

on an end ________

4.

Box Tossing	
on its bottom	𝍸 𝍸 𝍸 𝍸 ||
on its top	𝍸 𝍸 𝍸 𝍸 𝍸 |||
on an end	|||
on a side	𝍸 ||

Total number of tosses: ____
Probability of box landing:

on its bottom ________

on its top ________

on an end ________

on a side ________

If you toss a cap from a tube of toothpaste, there are three possible outcomes:

open end up

open end down

on its side

Conduct an experiment to find the likelihood of each possible outcome.
Ask a family member to do the experiment too.
Record your data in the first chart. Ask your partner to use the second chart.

1. a) Predict the number of times each outcome will occur in 50 trials. Record your predictions.

b) Toss the cap 50 times. Record the results.

c) Express each result as a fraction of the total number of tosses.

Person 1:

Possible Outcome	Prediction	Tally	Fraction (out of 50)
open end up			
open end down			
on its side			

Person 2:

Possible Outcome	Prediction	Tally	Fraction (out of 50)
open end up			
open end down			
on its side			

2. Combine your data with your partner's data.
Record your combined data.

Combined Results

Possible Outcome	Total Number of Times	Fraction (out of 100)
open end up		
open end down		
on its side		

3. What conclusion can you draw from this experiment? ____________

____

FAMILY NOTE: Your child is learning to determine experimental probability and to express probabilities as fractions. In subsequent lessons, your child will use this knowledge of experimental probability as he or she learns about theoretical probability.

Determining Theoretical Probability

Express the probability of each outcome as a fraction.

1.

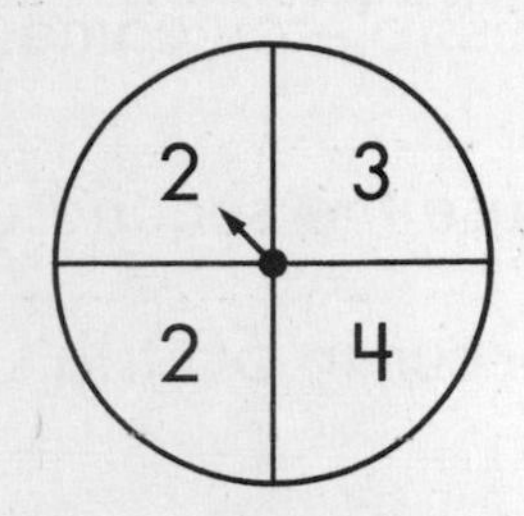

State the probability of spinning:

a) 2 ________ **b)** an even number ____

c) 4 ________ **d)** an odd number ______

2.

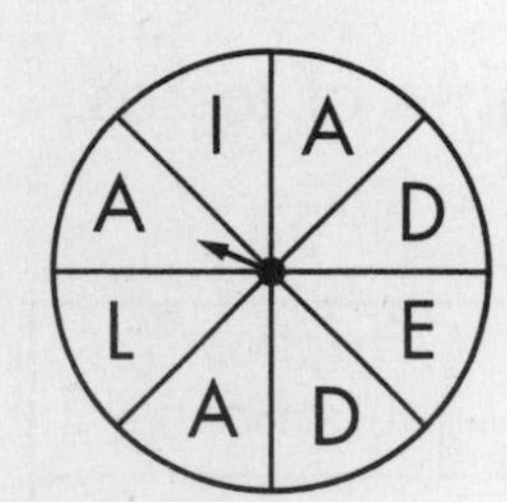

State the probability of spinning:

a) A ________ **b)** a vowel __________

c) D ________ **d)** a consonant _______

3.

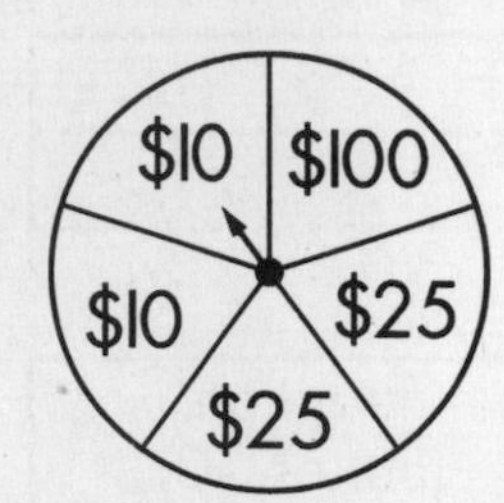

State the probability of spinning:

a) $10 ______ **b)** $100 __________

c) $25 ______ **d)** less than $10 _______

4.

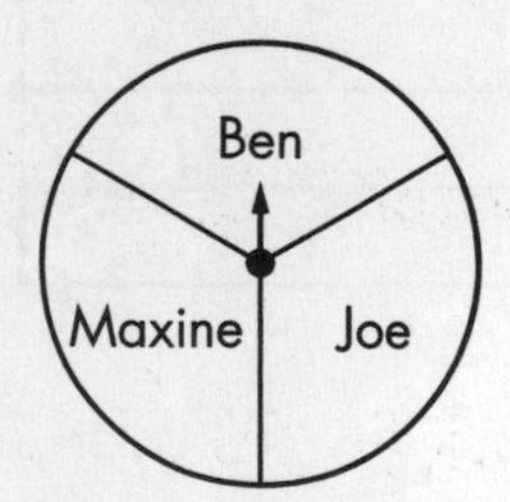

State the probability of spinning:

a) Ben ______ **b)** a boy's name _______

c) Maxine ___ **d)** a name __________

5.

State the probability of spinning:

a) a prime number ____________________

b) a composite number ______________

6.

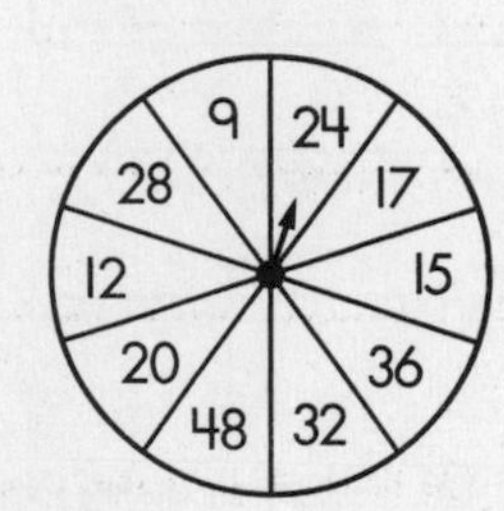

State the probability of spinning:

a) a multiple of 3 __________________

b) a multiple of 4 __________________

c) a common multiple of 3 and 4 _______

1. Express as a fraction the probability of spinning each outcome.

What is the probability of spinning:

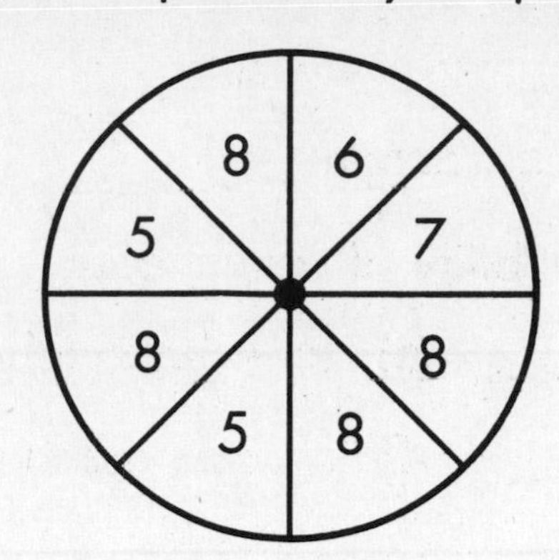

a) a 5? ________

b) a 6? ________

c) a 7? ________

d) an 8? ________

2. Use the spinner above.

Possible Outcome	Prediction	Tally	Fraction
5			
6			
7			
8			

a) Predict the number of times each outcome will occur in 50 trials. Record your predictions in the chart.

b) On the spinner, spin a paper clip around a pencil tip 50 times. Tally the results.

c) Express each result as a fraction of the total number of spins.

3. Compare the results of the experiment with the probabilities you calculated.____

____

____

FAMILY NOTE: Your child is learning to calculate the theoretical probabilities of outcomes and to compare them with experimental outcomes. You may want to have your child do the spinner experiment a second time and combine the second set of results with the first. The combined results may come closer to the calculated probabilities.

Connecting Probabilities with Outcomes

Match each probability to a spinner below.

1. The probability of spinning a 6 is $\frac{3}{5}$. ____________________

2. The probability of spinning a 5 is $\frac{1}{2}$. ____________________

3. The probability of spinning an even number is $\frac{5}{8}$. ____________

4. The probability of spinning a 1 is $\frac{2}{3}$. ____________________

5. The probability of spinning an odd number is $\frac{3}{4}$. ____________

6. The probability of spinning a multiple of 3 is $\frac{1}{3}$. ____________

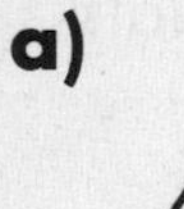

a)

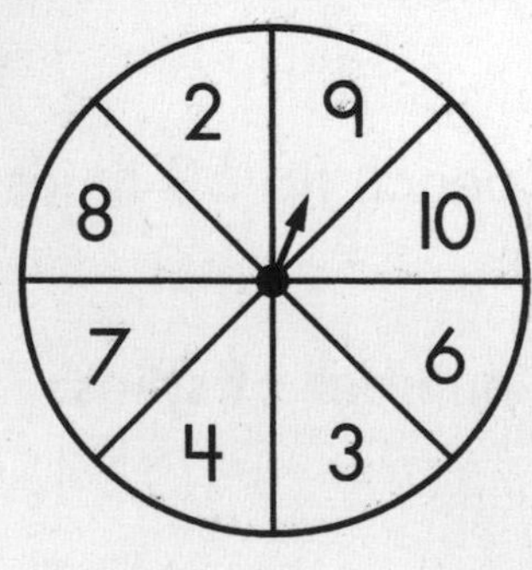

b)

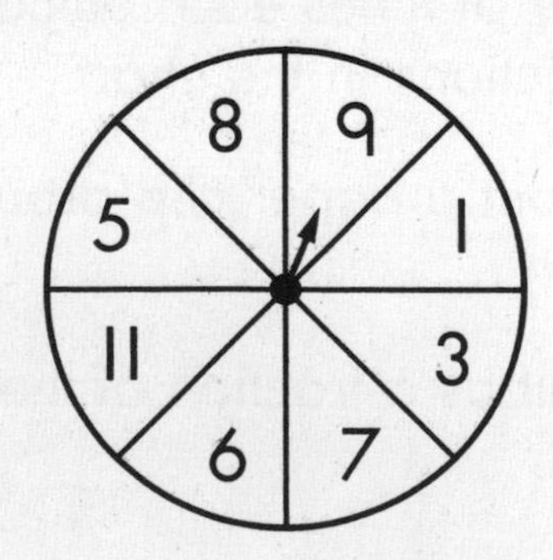

c)

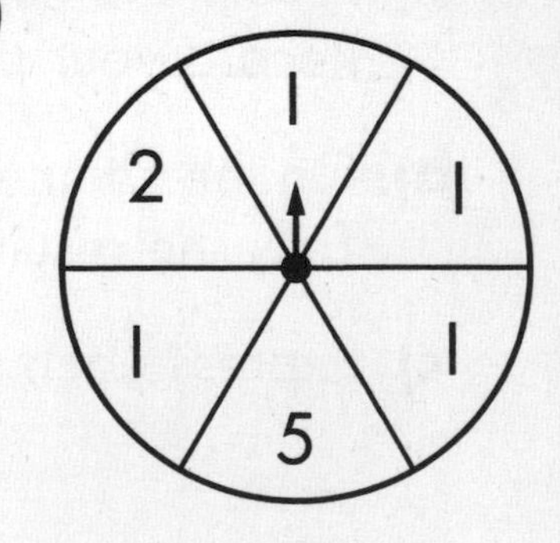

d)

e)

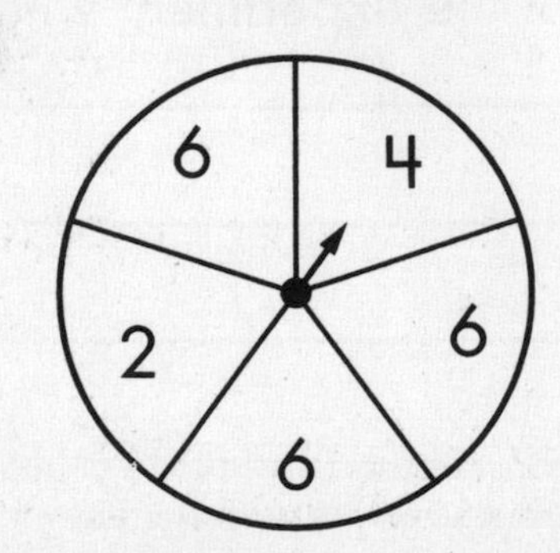

f)

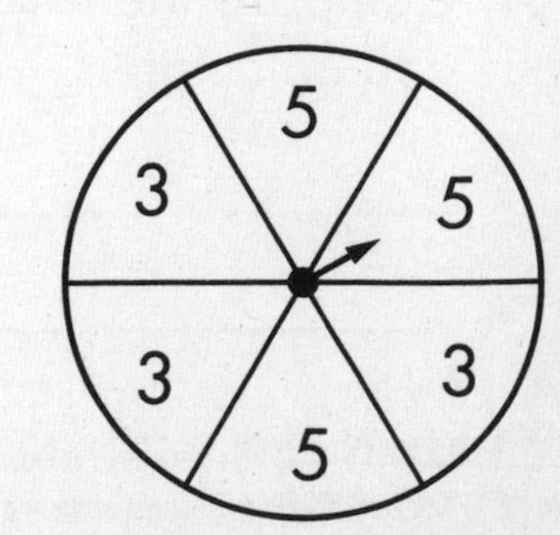

Write letters on the spinners to match the probabilities.

1.

The probability of spinning a B is $\frac{1}{2}$.

2.

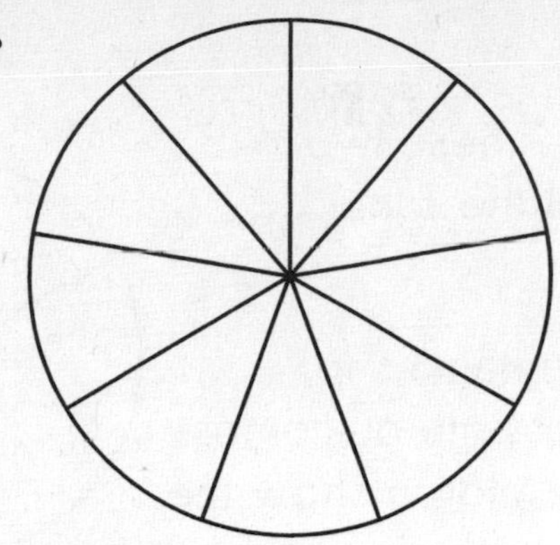

The probability of spinning a J is $\frac{2}{3}$.

3.

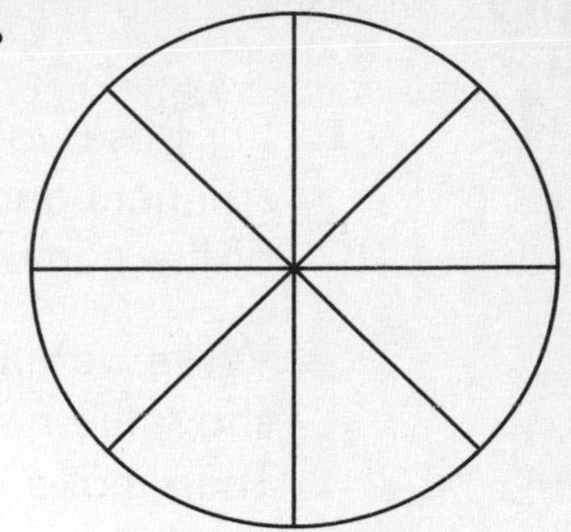

The probability of spinning a Z is $\frac{1}{4}$.

4.

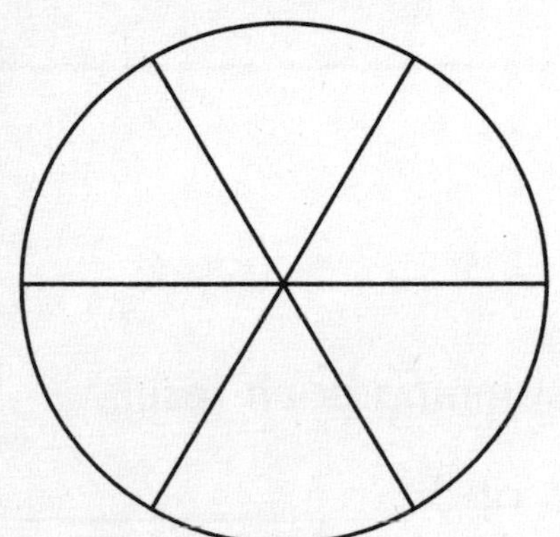

The probability of spinning a G is $\frac{1}{3}$.

5.

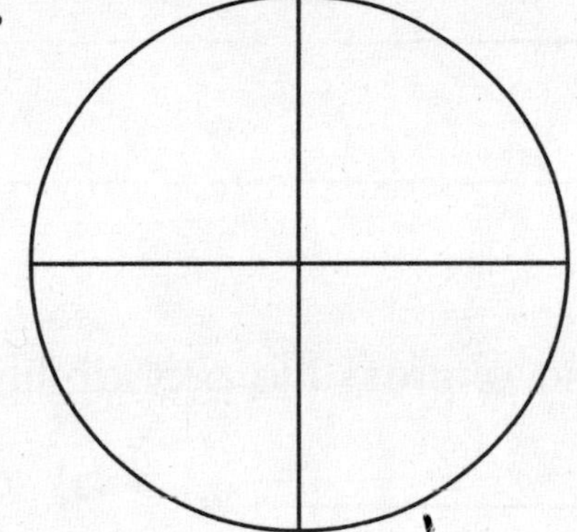

The probability of spinning a vowel is $\frac{1}{2}$.

6.

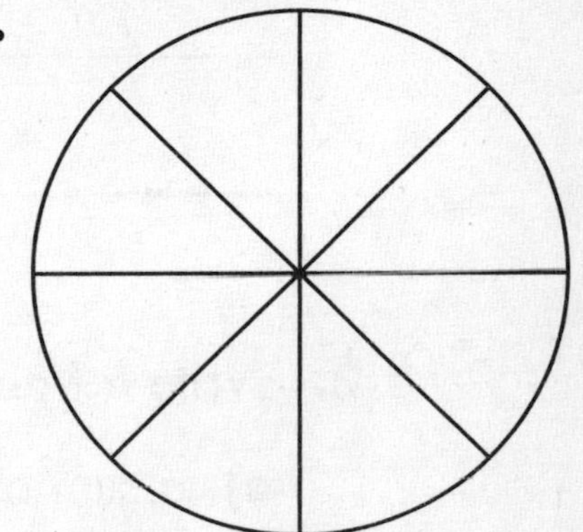

The probability of spinning a capital letter is $\frac{3}{4}$.

7.

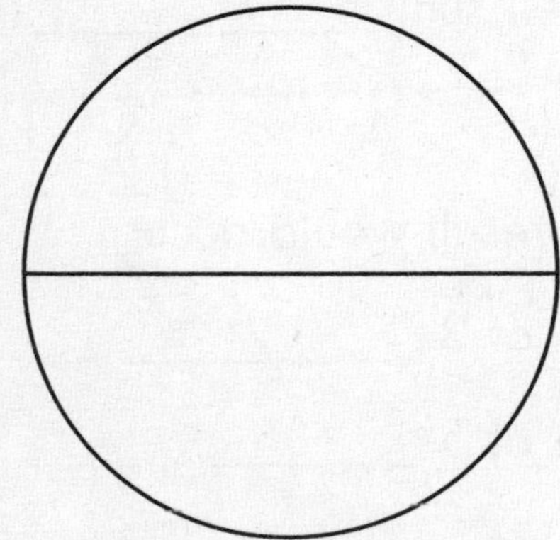

The probability of spinning a C is $\frac{1}{1}$.

8.

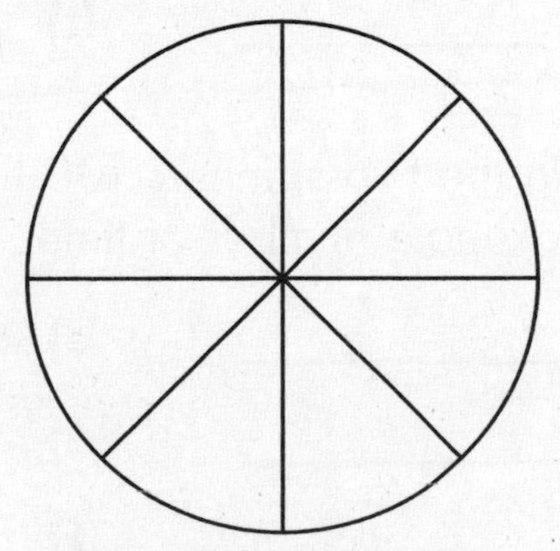

The probability of spinning a Q is $\frac{0}{1}$.

9.

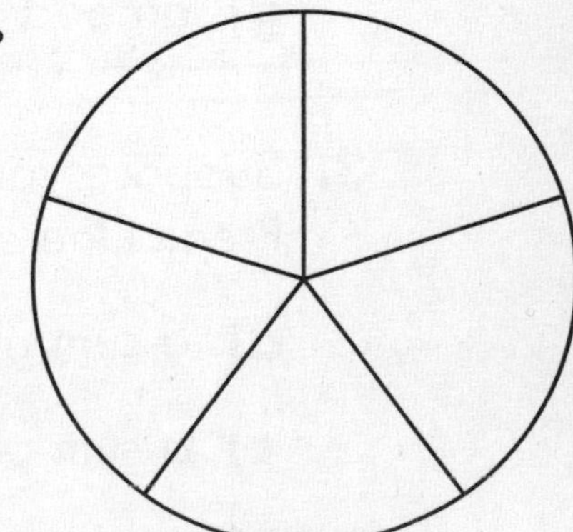

The probability of spinning a P is $\frac{2}{5}$.

FAMILY NOTE: Your child is learning to connect given probabilities to possible sets of outcomes. To do this work, your child needs to understand that a probability written as a fraction can have other fraction names. For example, $\frac{2}{3}$ can also be written as $\frac{4}{6}$, $\frac{8}{12}$, and so on.

Predicting Results

1. Suppose you spin these two spinners and find the sum of the numbers.

   Write addition sentences to show the nine possible outcomes. Then make a line plot to show the number of ways each sum can occur.

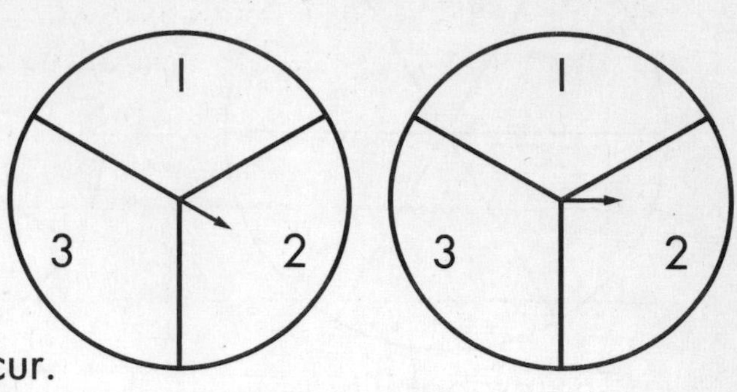

______ ______ ______

______ ______ ______

______ ______ ______

2. Write a fraction to express the probability of spinning each result.

   a) a sum of 2 ______ **b)** a sum of 3 ______

   c) a sum of 4 ______ **d)** a sum of 5 ______

   e) a sum of 6 ______ **f)** a double ______

   g) an odd sum ______ **h)** an even sum ______

3. Suppose you spin the two spinners 100 times. Predict the approximate number of times each result would occur.

   a) a sum of 2 ______ **b)** a sum of 3 ______

   c) a sum of 4 ______ **d)** a sum of 5 ______

   e) a sum of 6 ______ **f)** a double ______

   g) an odd sum ______ **h)** an even sum ______

76/3

1. Suppose you spin these two spinners and find the product of the numbers.

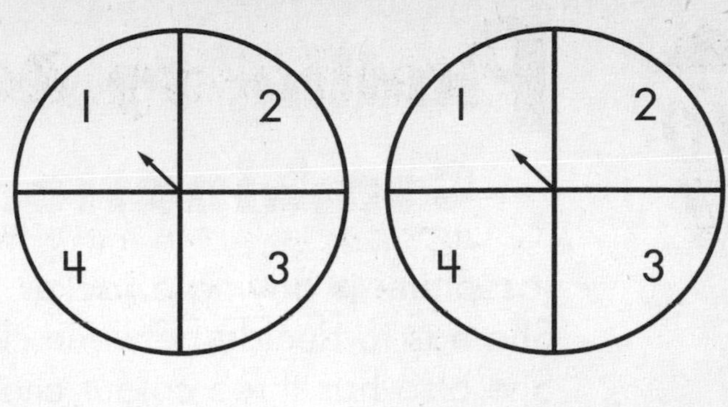

Write multiplication sentences to show the 16 possible outcomes.

__________ __________ __________ __________

__________ __________ __________ __________

__________ __________ __________ __________

__________ __________ __________ __________

2. Write a fraction to express the probability of spinning each product.

a) 1 ________ **b)** 2 ________ **c)** 3 ________

d) 4 ________ **e)** 6 ________ **f)** 8 ________

g) 9 ________ **h)** 12 ________ **i)** 16 ________

3. Write a fraction to express the probability of spinning each result.

a) an even product ________ **b)** an odd product ________

c) a product greater than 6 ____ **d)** a product less than 4 ____

4. Suppose you spin the spinners 100 times.
Predict the approximate number of times each product would occur.

a) 1 ________ **b)** 2 ________ **c)** 3 ________

d) 4 ________ **e)** 6 ________ **f)** 8 ________

g) 9 ________ **h)** 12 ________ **i)** 16 ________

5. Suppose you spin the spinners 500 times.
Predict the approximate number of times each product would occur.

a) 1 ________ **b)** 2 ________ **c)** 3 ________

d) 4 ________ **e)** 6 ________ **f)** 8 ________

g) 9 ________ **h)** 12 ________ **i)** 16 ________

FAMILY NOTE: Your child is learning to use calculated probabilities to predict experimental results. This helps to consolidate your child's understanding of probability concepts.

Finding Probabilities for Combinations

Josephine is buying a jacket.
She has to decide between cloth and suede.
She also has three colour choices — black, red, or green.

1. Make an organized list to show all the possible jacket choices.

2. How many choices does Josephine have? ______________

3. Suppose Josephine decides on a suede jacket. Now how many choices does she have? ______________

4. Suppose Josephine also has to decide whether to buy a lined or unlined jacket. Make a tree diagram to show all the possible cloth and suede jacket choices.

5. How many choices are there now? ______________

EARLY BIRD SPECIAL

Eggs, Juice, and Toast $2.99

Eggs: scrambled or poached
Juice: apple, orange, or tomato
Toast: whole wheat, white, or rye

1. Make a tree diagram to show all the possible Early Bird Specials.

2. How many different orders are possible? ____________________

3. What is the probability that an order will include each of these choices?

a) scrambled eggs __________ **b)** scrambled eggs and white toast _______

c) orange juice ____________ **d)** rye toast ______________

e) whole wheat toast and tomato juice __________________

f) apple juice and white toast __________________

g) eggs __________________ **h)** juice and rye toast __________________

i) apple juice, whole wheat toast, and poached eggs ____________________

FAMILY NOTE: Your child is learning to use tree diagrams and organized lists to represent and count all the outcomes in a given situation. These skills are useful in solving "combinations" problems such as the one on this page.

Calculating Perimeter

Calculate the perimeter of each figure without adding all the side lengths.

1.

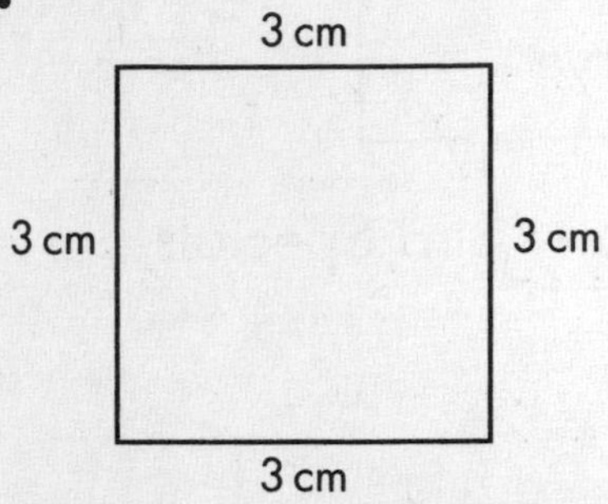

2.

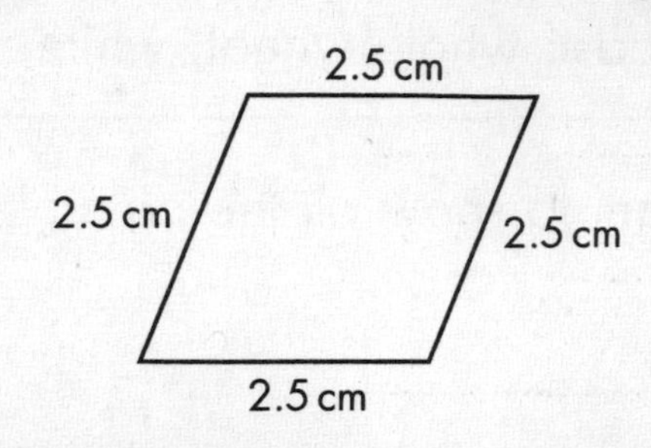

3.

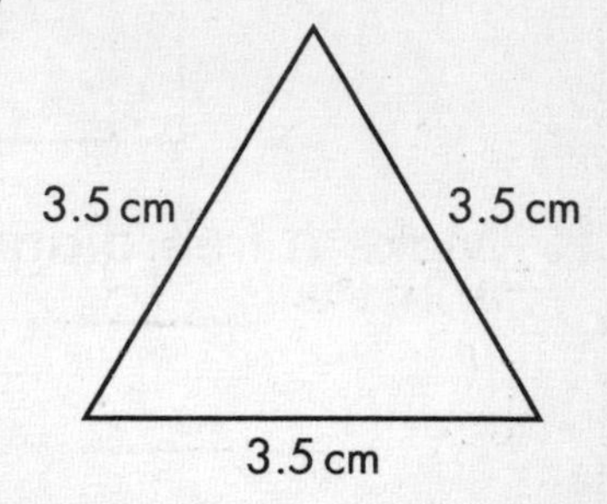

4.

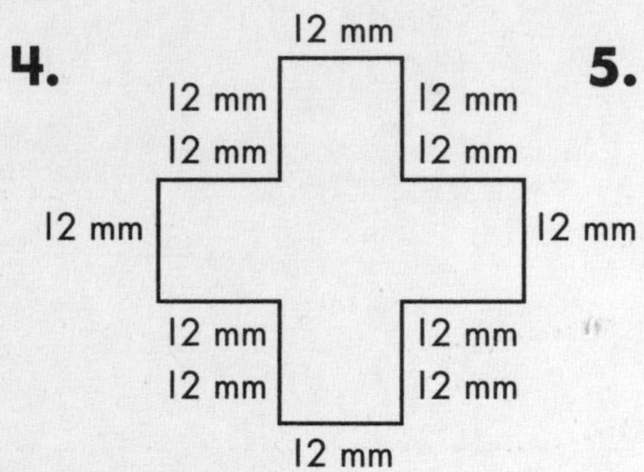

5.

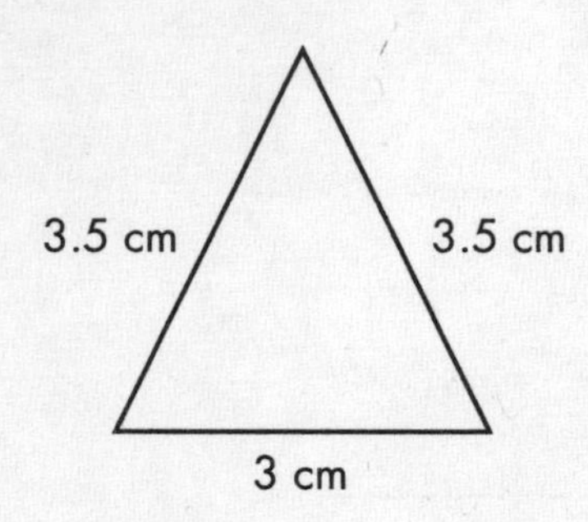

6.

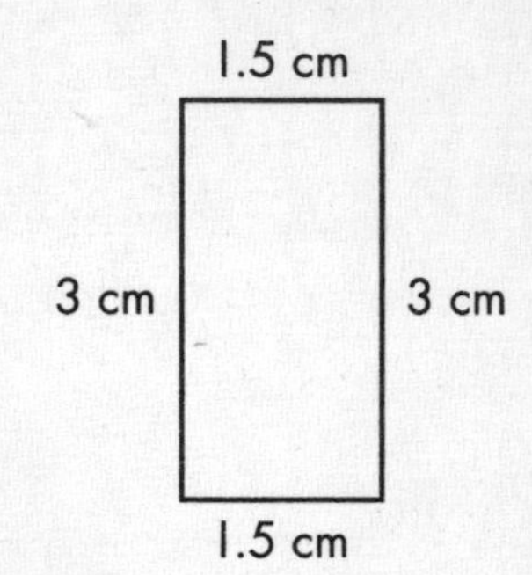

7.

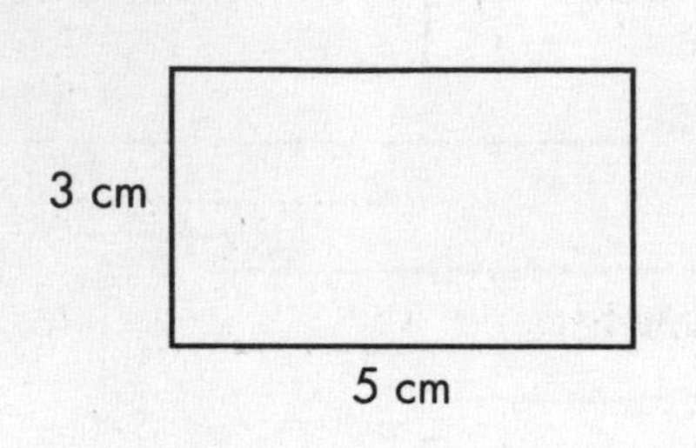

8.

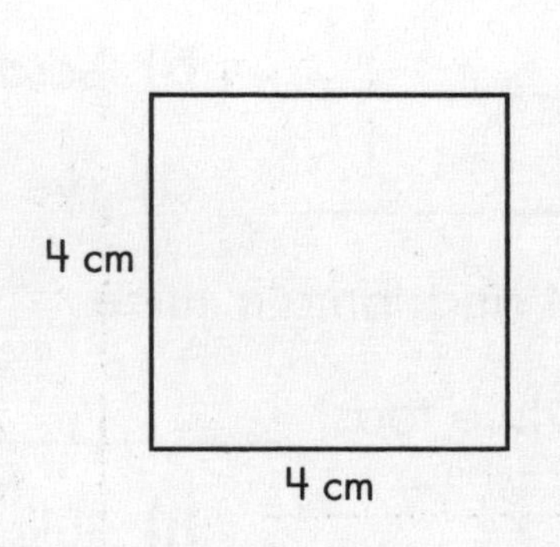

9.

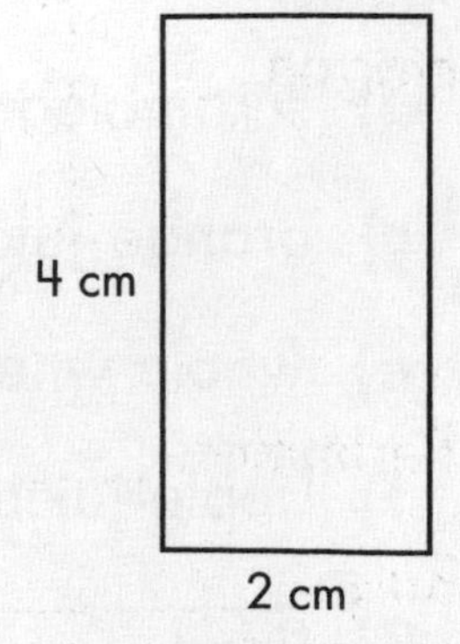

Calculate the perimeter of each figure.
Write a rule to tell how you found the perimeter.

1. square

3.5 cm

Perimeter: 14.0 cm

Rule: 3.5 × 4

2. equilateral triangle

3.5 cm

Perimeter: 10.5 cm

Rule: 3.5 × 3

3. isosceles triangle

3 cm

4.5 cm

Perimeter: 10.5 cm

Rule: 3 × 2 + 4.5

4. rectangle

2 cm

6 cm

Perimeter: 16 cm

Rule: 6 × 2 + 2 × 2

5. regular octagon

1.5 cm

Perimeter: 12.0 cm

Rule: 1.5 × 8

6. rectangle

3.5 cm

3 cm

Perimeter: 11 cm

Rule: 3 × 2 + 3.5 × 2

FAMILY NOTE: Your child is learning to calculate perimeter by applying rules. Each rule your child writes should reflect the method she or he used. For example, to find the perimeter of the square, the rule could be *perimeter* = 4 × *the side length*.

Calculating Area

Write a multiplication sentence to describe the area of each rectangle.

1.

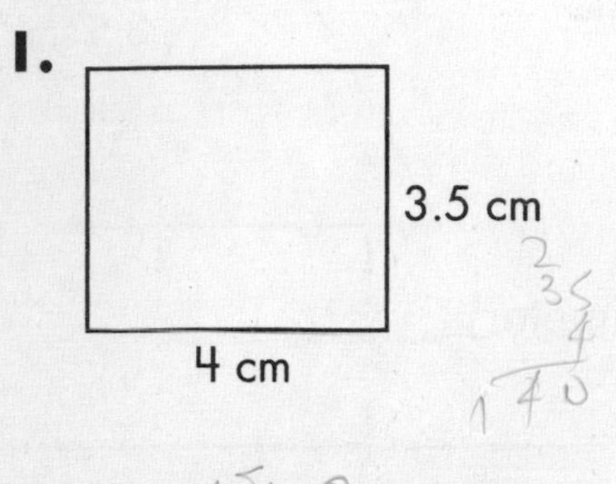

2.

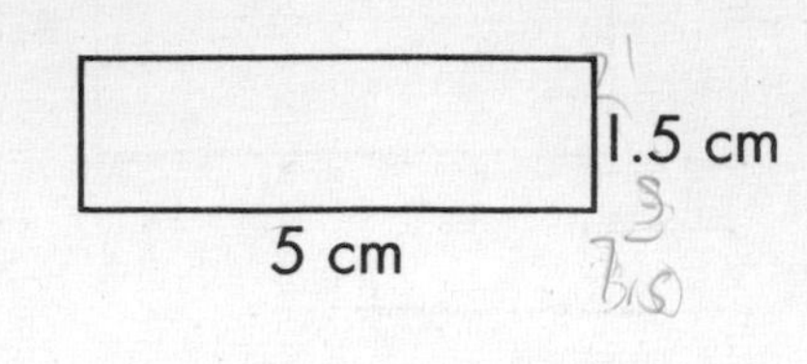

3.

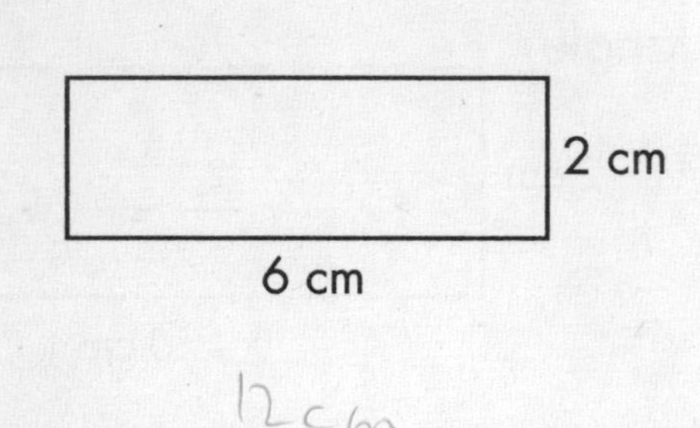

4.

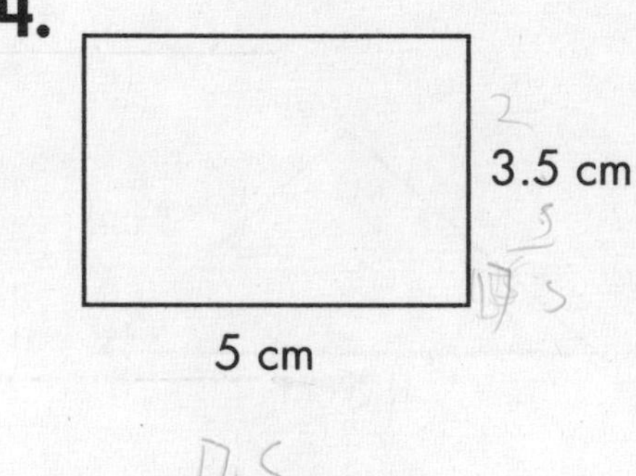

Calculate the area of the shaded part of each rectangle.
Show all your work.

5.

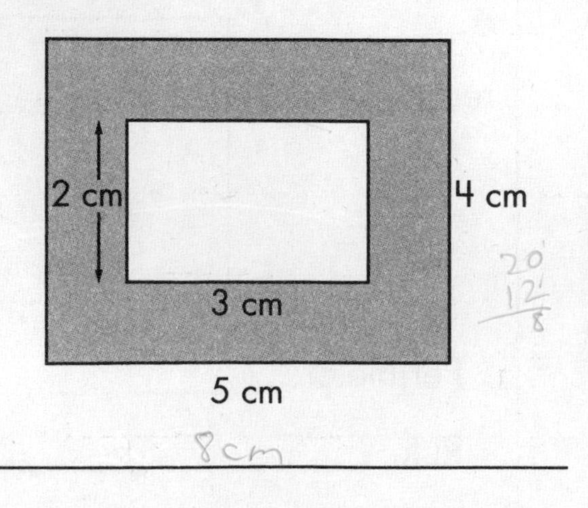

6.

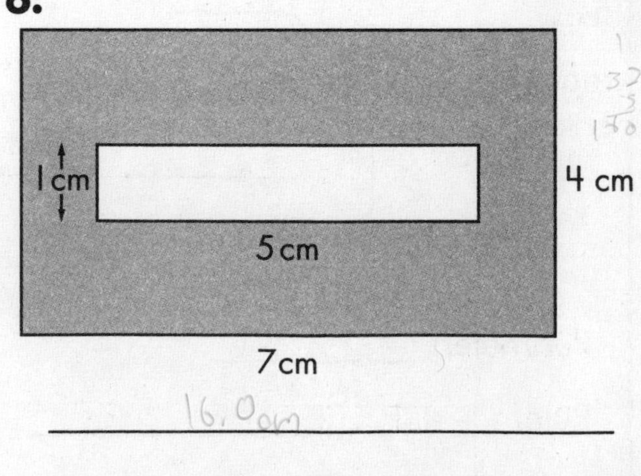

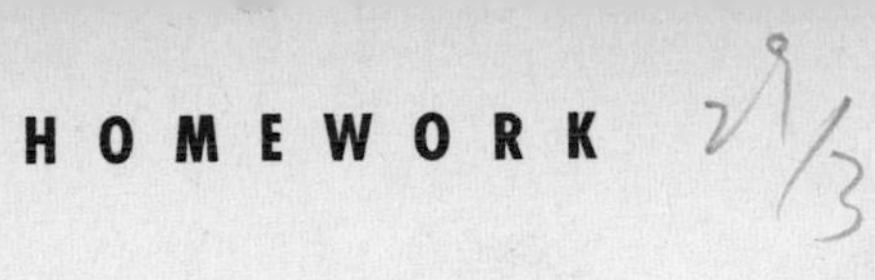

Draw a rectangle that has each area.
Inside each rectangle, write a multiplication sentence to describe the area.

1. 15 cm^2 **2.** 24 cm^2 **3.** 56 cm^2 **4.** 20 cm^2

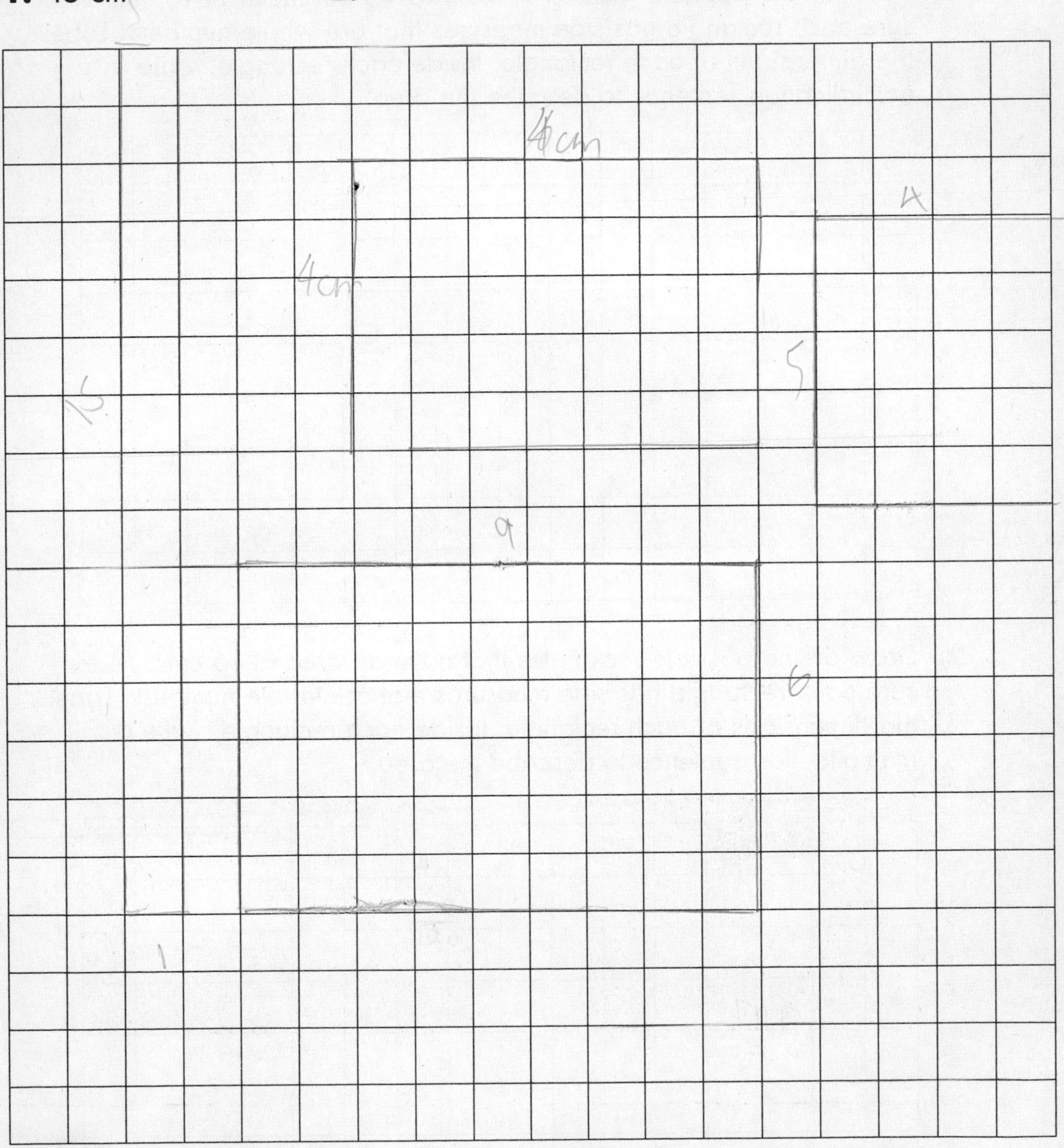

FAMILY NOTE: Your child has learned to use the rule *Area* = *length* × *width* to find the area of a rectangle. Ask how your child found the dimensions of the rectangles on this page.

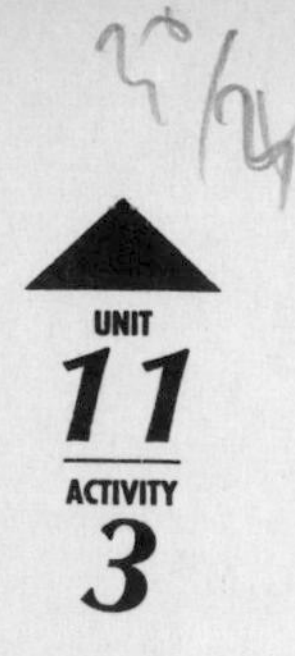

Relating Area and Perimeter

1. Draw all the possible rectangles that have a perimeter of 16 cm. Make sure each rectangle has side measures that are whole numbers. Label the dimensions of each rectangle. Inside each rectangle, write a multiplication sentence to describe the area.

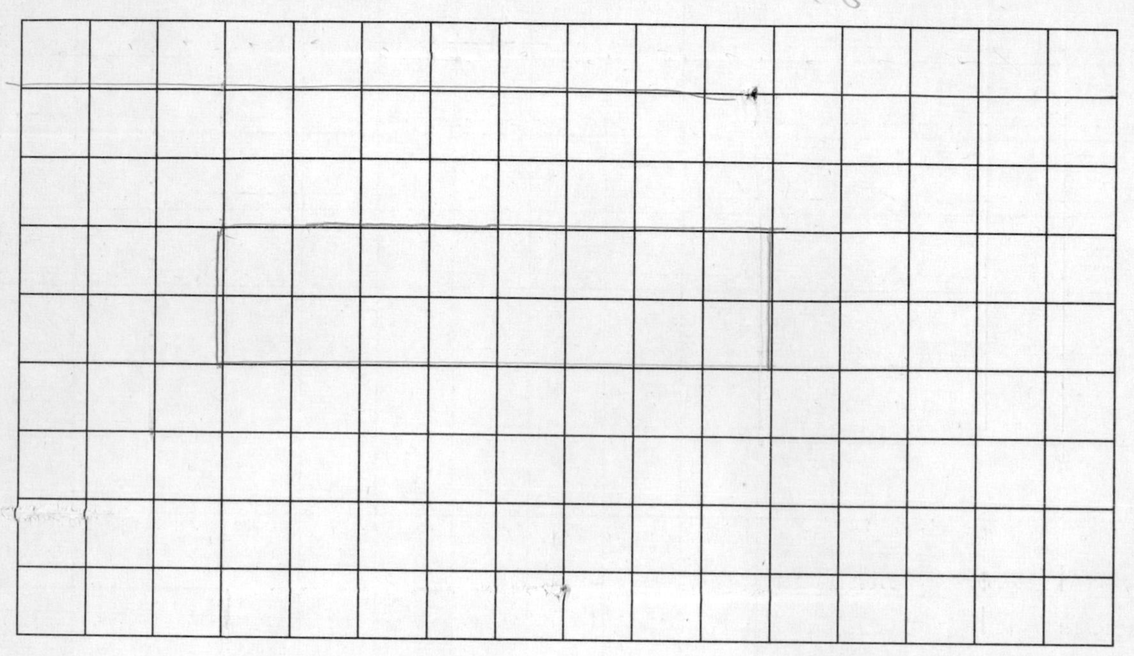

2. Draw all the possible rectangles that have an area of 16 cm^2. Make sure each rectangle has side measures that are whole numbers. Label the dimensions of each rectangle. Inside each rectangle, write a multiplication sentence to describe the area.

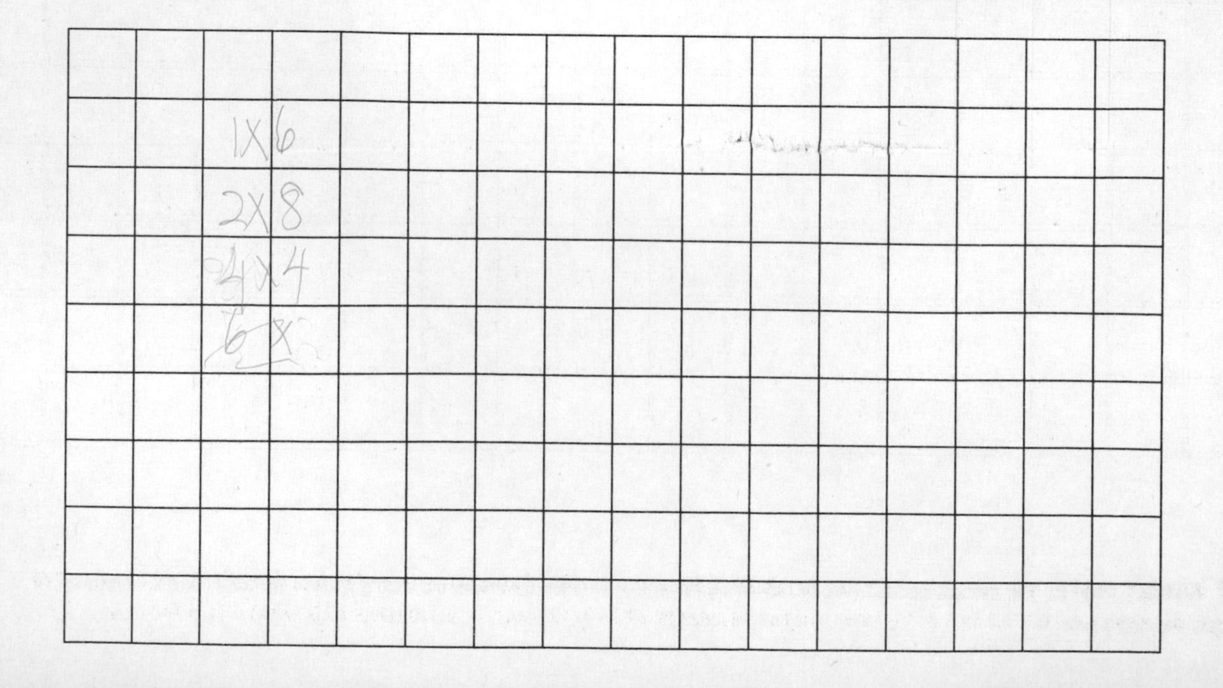

1. Draw the rectangle with the greatest possible perimeter for each area.
Use side lengths that are whole numbers.
Label the dimensions.

10 cm^2 13 cm^2 16 cm^2

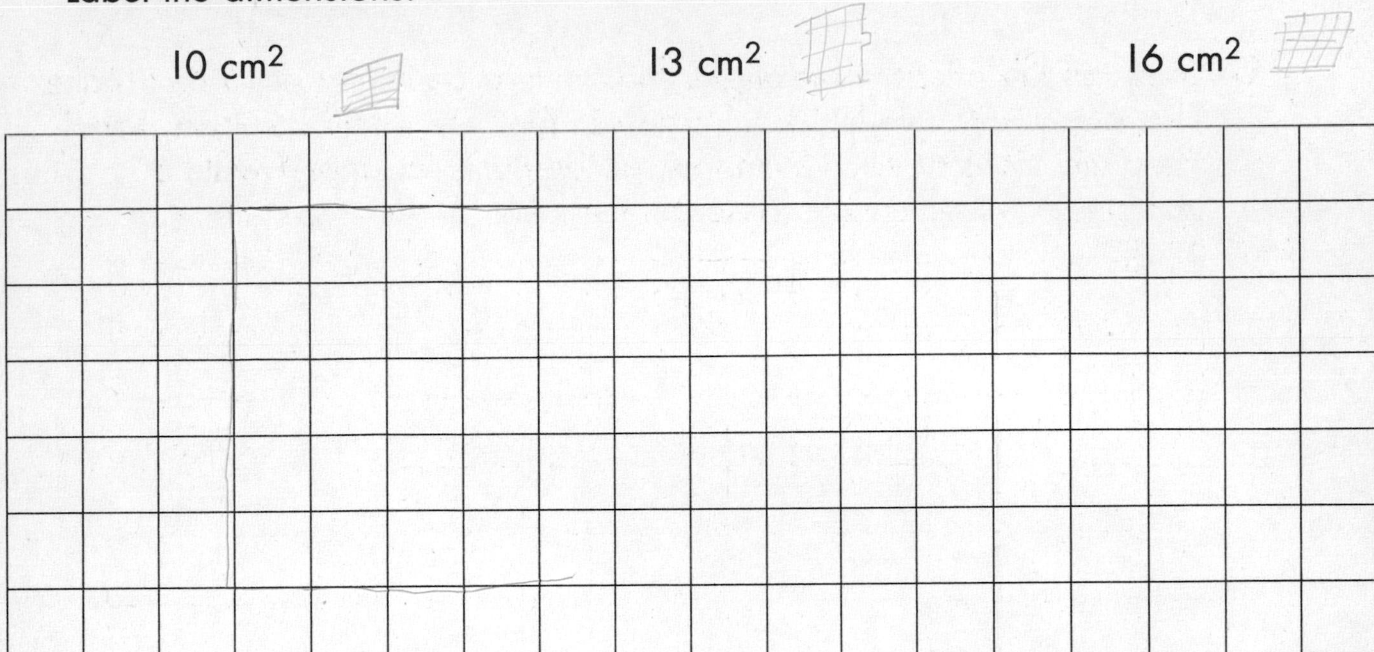

2. Draw the rectangle with the greatest possible area for each perimeter.
Use side lengths that are whole numbers.
Inside each rectangle, write a multiplication sentence to show the area.

18 cm 14 cm 20 cm

FAMILY NOTE: Your child has been exploring the relationships between the areas and perimeters of rectangles. He or she has learned, for example, that rectangles with a given perimeter can have different areas, and that the rectangle with the greatest area for that perimeter will be closest in shape to a square.

Computation Skills Bank

Addition Facts

1.	9 + 3 = ___	3 + 4 = ___	6 + 4 = ___	3 + 9 = ___
2.	8 + 5 = ___	8 + 3 = ___	8 + 8 = ___	5 + 3 = ___
3.	4 + 5 = ___	9 + 9 = ___	2 + 9 = ___	4 + 9 = ___
4.	7 + 9 = ___	4 + 8 = ___	5 + 5 = ___	9 + 2 = ___
5.	0 + 10 = ___	5 + 8 = ___	2 + 7 = ___	6 + 9 = ___
6.	8 + 4 = ___	2 + 7 = ___	4 + 8 = ___	10 + 0 = ___
7.	7 + 6 = ___	4 + 6 = ___	3 + 8 = ___	9 + 7 = ___
8.	8 + 6 = ___	9 + 8 = ___	9 + 1 = ___	3 + 7 = ___
9.	8 + 2 = ___	9 + 5 = ___	6 + 7 = ___	6 + 6 = ___
10.	9 + 6 = ___	8 + 7 = ___	4 + 2 = ___	6 + 5 = ___
11.	0 + 9 = ___	5 + 7 = ___	2 + 8 = ___	5 + 9 = ___
12.	1 + 4 = ___	6 + 8 = ___	9 + 8 = ___	7 + 8 = ___
13.	9 + 4 = ___	7 + 7 = ___	4 + 7 = ___	7 + 5 = ___
14.	7 + 9 = ___	1 + 9 = ___	7 + 8 = ___	8 + 9 = ___
15.	7 + 3 = ___	9 + 9 = ___	6 + 8 = ___	5 + 6 = ___

Subtraction Facts

1. 11 − 2 = 3 | 17 − 9 = 8 | 13 − 4 = 9 | 9 − 1 = 8

2. 14 − 6 = 8 | 10 − 6 = 4 | 14 − 5 = 9 | 12 − 4 = 8

3. 9 − 4 = 5 | 12 − 3 = 9 | 9 − 9 = 0 | 10 − 5 = 5

4. 12 − 5 = 7 | 9 − 2 = 7 | 13 − 5 = 8 | 14 − 8 = 6

5. 10 − 4 = 6 | 13 − 9 = 2 | 11 − 9 = 2 | 11 − 8 = 3

6. 11 − 3 = 8 | 17 − 8 = 9 | 16 − 8 = 8 | 10 − 10 = 0

7. 14 − 7 = 7 | 9 − 8 = 1 | 8 − 5 = 3 | 16 − 7 = 9

8. 16 − 9 = 7 | 13 − 6 = 7 | 10 − 1 = 9 | 9 − 5 = 4

9. 10 − 8 = 2 | 15 − 7 = 8 | 7 − 4 = 3 | 11 − 7 = 4

10. 18 − 9 = 9 | 8 − 3 = 5 | 9 − 7 = 2 | 12 − 7 = 5

11. 12 − 6 = 6 | 12 − 9 = 3 | 10 − 7 = 3 | 14 − 9 = 3

12. 9 − 3 = 6 | 13 − 7 = 6 | 15 − 9 = 4 | 10 − 3 = 7

13. 11 − 4 = 7 | 10 − 9 = 1 | 12 − 8 = 4 | 15 − 6 = 9

14. 10 − 2 = 8 | 7 − 5 = 2 | 11 − 6 = 5 | 13 − 8 = 5

15. 15 − 8 = 7 | 11 − 5 = 6 | 6 − 0 = 0 | 9 − 6 = 3

Multiplication Facts (1)

1.	$9 \times 5 =$ 45	$5 \times 9 =$ 45	$5 \times 6 =$ 30	$1 \times 7 =$ 7
2.	$5 \times 8 =$ 40	$2 \times 7 =$ 14	$4 \times 0 =$ 0	$6 \times 9 =$ 54
3.	$3 \times 7 =$ 21	$9 \times 7 =$ 16	$6 \times 8 =$ 48	$8 \times 7 =$ 56
4.	$9 \times 6 =$ 54	$6 \times 5 =$ 30	$8 \times 5 =$ 40	$6 \times 6 =$ 38
5.	$8 \times 9 =$ 72	$8 \times 4 =$ 32	$8 \times 3 =$ 24	$1 \times 8 =$ 8
6.	$9 \times 4 =$ 36	$9 \times 9 =$ 81	$7 \times 8 =$ 56	$0 \times 5 =$ 0
7.	$4 \times 6 =$ 24	$2 \times 8 =$ 16	$4 \times 3 =$ 12	$4 \times 8 =$ 32
8.	$7 \times 9 =$ 62	$9 \times 3 =$ 27	$7 \times 6 =$ 42	$2 \times 5 =$ 10
9.	$7 \times 5 =$ 35	$3 \times 9 =$ 27	$3 \times 5 =$ 15	$6 \times 7 =$ 42
10.	$9 \times 8 =$ 72	$2 \times 6 =$ 12	$3 \times 4 =$ 12	$2 \times 4 =$ 8
11.	$3 \times 6 =$ 24	$8 \times 6 =$ 48	$7 \times 3 =$ 21	$6 \times 3 =$ 24
12.	$6 \times 4 =$ 24	$8 \times 8 =$ 64	$2 \times 9 =$ 18	$5 \times 7 =$ 35
13.	$5 \times 3 =$ 15	$5 \times 5 =$ 25	$4 \times 5 =$ 20	$4 \times 9 =$ 36
14.	$1 \times 9 =$ 9	$5 \times 4 =$ 20	$3 \times 8 =$ 24	$1 \times 6 =$ 6
15.	$7 \times 4 =$ 24	$4 \times 7 =$ 28	$4 \times 4 =$ 16	$7 \times 7 =$ 49

Multiplication Facts (2)

Complete the table.

×	0	1	2	3	4	5	6	7	8	9
0	0	0	0	0	0	0	0	0	0	0
1	0	1	2	3	4	5	6	7	8	9
2	0	2	4	6	8	10	12	14	16	18
3	0	3	6	9	12	15	18	21	24	27
4	0	4	8	12	16	20	24	28	32	34
5	0	5	10	15	20	25	30	35	400	45
6	0	6	12	18	24	30	36	42	48	56
7	0	7	14	21	28	35	42	49	56	63
8	0	8	18	24	32	40	48	56	64	72
9	0	9	20	27	36	45	54	63	72	84

Complete this mixed-up table.

×	5	9	2	1	7	0	3	4	8	6
3	15	27	6	3	21	0	9	12	24	18
6	30	56	12	6	42	0	18	24	48	36

Multiplication Turnaround Facts

Multiply. Then write the turnaround fact.

1. 2 × 7 = ______	6 × 5 = ______	8 × 9 = ______
2. 8 × 5 = ______	7 × 6 = ______	4 × 7 = ______
3. 9 × 7 = ______	6 × 4 = ______	2 × 9 = ______
4. 7 × 8 = ______	8 × 6 = ______	9 × 3 = ______
5. 5 × 7 = ______	4 × 3 = ______	6 × 9 = ______
6. 6 × 3 = ______	9 × 5 = ______	6 × 2 = ______
7. 5 × 4 = ______	4 × 9 = ______	8 × 4 = ______
8. 2 × 8 = ______	1 × 9 = ______	3 × 8 = ______
9. 7 × 3 = ______	4 × 0 = ______	3 × 2 = ______

Division Facts (1)

1.	36 ÷ 9 = ___	24 ÷ 6 = ___	24 ÷ 4 = ___	42 ÷ 7 = ___
2.	64 ÷ 8 = ___	30 ÷ 5 = ___	21 ÷ 3 = ___	8 ÷ 8 = ___
3.	24 ÷ 3 = ___	16 ÷ 8 = ___	27 ÷ 9 = ___	12 ÷ 6 = ___
4.	35 ÷ 5 = ___	7 ÷ 7 = ___	18 ÷ 6 = ___	20 ÷ 4 = ___
5.	6 ÷ 6 = ___	18 ÷ 3 = ___	72 ÷ 8 = ___	5 ÷ 5 = ___
6.	15 ÷ 3 = ___	49 ÷ 7 = ___	14 ÷ 7 = ___	18 ÷ 9 = ___
7.	24 ÷ 8 = ___	15 ÷ 5 = ___	63 ÷ 9 = ___	10 ÷ 5 = ___
8.	45 ÷ 9 = ___	40 ÷ 5 = ___	56 ÷ 8 = ___	16 ÷ 4 = ___
9.	35 ÷ 7 = ___	28 ÷ 4 = ___	30 ÷ 6 = ___	28 ÷ 7 = ___
10.	25 ÷ 5 = ___	72 ÷ 9 = ___	56 ÷ 7 = ___	45 ÷ 5 = ___
11.	9 ÷ 9 = ___	42 ÷ 6 = ___	20 ÷ 5 = ___	8 ÷ 4 = ___
12.	48 ÷ 6 = ___	32 ÷ 8 = ___	12 ÷ 4 = ___	36 ÷ 6 = ___
13.	12 ÷ 3 = ___	32 ÷ 4 = ___	21 ÷ 7 = ___	40 ÷ 8 = ___
14.	48 ÷ 8 = ___	54 ÷ 6 = ___	81 ÷ 9 = ___	63 ÷ 7 = ___
15.	54 ÷ 9 = ___	9 ÷ 3 = ___	36 ÷ 4 = ___	27 ÷ 3 = ___

Division Facts (2)

1.	9)63	9)18	7)49	8)72	6)36
2.	3)15	7)42	9)54	5)45	7)7
3.	8)24	6)42	6)30	8)48	8)32
4.	9)45	5)35	7)14	3)21	5)15
5.	5)20	8)72	8)16	5)40	6)12
6.	6)18	7)21	4)28	9)81	6)48
7.	3)27	9)36	8)64	6)24	9)27
8.	8)40	4)32	3)36	8)56	7)28
9.	3)18	9)72	7)35	4)36	6)54

Division Partner Facts

Divide. Then write the partner fact.

1.	$72 \div 9 =$ 8 $72 \div 8 = 9$	$24 \div 3 =$ 8	$18 \div 9 =$ 2
2.	$36 \div 9 =$ 4	$63 \div 7 =$ 9	$56 \div 8 =$ 7
3.	$54 \div 6 =$ 9	$20 \div 4 =$ 5	$28 \div 7 =$ 4
4.	$21 \div 3 =$ 7	$30 \div 6 =$ 5	$12 \div 4 =$ 3
5.	$35 \div 7 =$ 6	$45 \div 5 =$ 5	$16 \div 8 =$ 2
6.	$24 \div 6 =$ 4	$14 \div 2 =$ 7	$48 \div 6 =$ 8
7.	$32 \div 4 =$ 6	$27 \div 9 =$ 3	$18 \div 3 =$ 6
8.	$40 \div 8 =$ 5	$42 \div 7 =$ 6	$12 \div 2 =$ 6
9.	$6 \div 6 =$ 1	$15 \div 5 =$ 3	$10 \div 5 =$ 2

Multiplication and Division Partner Facts (1)

Multiply. Then write the division partner fact.

1.	$9 \times 8 =$ 72 $72 \div 9 = 8$	$7 \times 5 =$ ____	$3 \times 9 =$ ____
2.	$8 \times 7 =$ ____	$6 \times 8 =$ ____	$4 \times 6 =$ ____
3.	$6 \times 6 =$ ____	$6 \times 7 =$ ____	$9 \times 5 =$ ____
4.	$8 \times 6 =$ ____	$9 \times 9 =$ ____	$4 \times 8 =$ ____
5.	$5 \times 3 =$ ____	$6 \times 1 =$ ____	$4 \times 5 =$ ____
6.	$3 \times 8 =$ ____	$7 \times 6 =$ ____	$9 \times 7 =$ ____
7.	$8 \times 4 =$ ____	$6 \times 5 =$ ____	$9 \times 6 =$ ____
8.	$6 \times 3 =$ ____	$2 \times 7 =$ ____	$8 \times 9 =$ ____
9.	$8 \times 8 =$ ____	$5 \times 2 =$ ____	$9 \times 4 =$ ____

Multiplication and Division Partner Facts (2)

Divide. Then write the multiplication partner fact.

1. 18 ÷ 9 = 2 9 × 2 = 18	63 ÷ 7 = 9	28 ÷ 7 = 4
2. 12 ÷ 4 = 3	54 ÷ 6 = 9	21 ÷ 3 = 7
3. 18 ÷ 3 = 6	49 ÷ 7 = 7	27 ÷ 9 = 3
4. 24 ÷ 8 = 3	9 ÷ 1 = 9	40 ÷ 8 = 5
5. 21 ÷ 7 = 3	16 ÷ 8 = 2	10 ÷ 2 = 5
6. 40 ÷ 5 = 8	14 ÷ 7 = 2	24 ÷ 6 = 4
7. 7 ÷ 1 = 7	25 ÷ 5 = 5	12 ÷ 6 = 2
8. 35 ÷ 5 = 7	45 ÷ 9 = 5	81 ÷ 9 = 9
9. 20 ÷ 5 = 4	12 ÷ 3 = 7	30 ÷ 5 = 6

Multiplication and Division Fact Families

Complete each family of facts.

1.
$9 \times 5 =$ 45 $45 \div 9 = 5$
$5 \times 9 = 45$ $45 \div 5 = 9$

2.
$7 \times 6 =$ 42

3.
$6 \times 4 =$ 24

4.
$8 \times 7 =$ 56

5.
$5 \times 6 =$ 30

6.
$7 \times 9 =$ 63

7.
$4 \times 9 =$ 36

8.
$8 \times 4 =$ 32

9.
$5 \times 7 =$ 35

10.
$8 \times 9 =$ 72

11.
$9 \times 6 =$ 54

12.
$4 \times 7 =$ 24

13.
$6 \times 8 =$ 48

14.
$3 \times 8 =$ 24

15.
$7 \times 3 =$ 21

16.
$2 \times 9 =$ 18

17.
$9 \times 9 =$ 81

18.
$6 \times 6 =$ 36

Strategies for Adding Whole Numbers

There are many ways to add whole numbers.
Here are some ways to add 9727 and 4895.

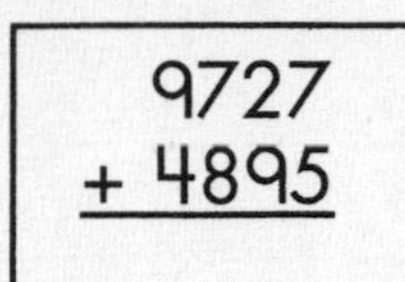

1. Add in parts.

$9000 + 4000 = 13\,000$
$700 + 800 = 1\,500$
$20 + 90 = 110$
$7 + 5 = 12$

$13\,000 + 1\,500 = 14\,500$
$110 + 12 = 122$
$14\,500 + 122 = 14\,622$

2. 4895 is 5 less than 4900.

If you add 5 to 4895 and subtract 5 from 9727, the answer will not change.

$9727 - 5 = 9722$
$4895 + 5 = 4900$

To add 9722 + 4900:

$9000 + 4000 = 13\,000$
$700 + 900 = 1\,600$

$14\,600 + 22 = 14\,622$

3.

Add the ones. Trade 10 ones for 1 ten. →	Add the tens. Trade 10 tens for 1 hundred. →	Add the hundreds. Trade 10 hundreds for 1 thousand. →	Add the thousands.
$\begin{array}{r} {\scriptstyle 1} \\ 9727 \\ +\,4895 \\ \hline 2 \end{array}$	$\begin{array}{r} {\scriptstyle 1\,1} \\ 9727 \\ +\,4895 \\ \hline 22 \end{array}$	$\begin{array}{r} {\scriptstyle 1\,1\,1} \\ 9727 \\ +\,4895 \\ \hline 622 \end{array}$	$\begin{array}{r} {\scriptstyle 1\,1\,1} \\ 9727 \\ +\,4895 \\ \hline 14622 \end{array}$

Addition: Whole Numbers (1)

1.	68 + 27	95 + 88	57 + 43	90 + 36
2.	58 + 99	76 + 24	23 + 82	47 + 25
3.	765 + 809	257 + 389	672 + 738	599 + 699
4.	941 + 685	900 + 850	387 + 668	476 + 674
5.	6351 + 8472	9645 + 3987	2085 + 5841	6979 + 5859
6.	7638 + 9738	8252 + 4978	6211 + 7233	9893 + 462

Addition: Whole Numbers (2)

1.	4869 + 7382	9784 + 7654	8239 + 9964	2020 + 9380
2.	5379 + 2468	7321 + 8499	6734 + 9521	3897 + 6825
3.	6257 8934 + 5073	2888 3690 + 928	1469 2738 + 1473	2486 7531 + 2121
4.	7817 5068 + 685	7521 8637 + 850	7382 5509 + 668	1284 3742 + 674
5.	785 632 272 + 396	158 462 737 + 180	628 356 874 + 902	400 385 621 + 733

Addition: Whole Numbers (3)

1.	285	721	473	976	286
	697	538	562	642	438
	+ 384	+ 68	+ 305	+ 837	+ 495

2.	727	368	209	724	391
	401	720	638	898	58
	+ 407	+ 493	+ 325	+ 200	+ 672

3.	4574	566	2327	5624	7680
	6438	2952	8613	848	9373
	+ 8125	+ 3413	+ 4938	+ 734	+ 4265

4.	5637	4998	5765	9876	6846
	1828	3277	8497	5304	3572
	+ 2456	+ 6582	+ 3029	+ 2512	+ 6543

5.	2863	1285	9752	4689	5674
	7604	6742	6485	3216	6852
	+ 381	+ 2345	+ 5673	+ 827	+ 4038

Addition: Whole Numbers (4)

Use mental math to find each sum.

1. 27 + 85 = ______ 68 + 37 = ______ 95 + 43 = ______

2. 38 + 62 = ______ 97 + 103 = ______ 32 + 49 = ______

3. 94 + 46 = ______ 73 + 25 = ______ 68 + 97 = ______

4. 200 + 165 = ______ 185 + 145 = ______ 233 + 457 = ______

5. 371 + 492 = ______ 425 + 175 = ______ 589 + 121 = ______

6. 735 + 265 = ______ 398 + 426 = ______ 709 + 289 = ______

7. 425 + 276 = ______ 585 + 116 = ______ 375 + 226 = ______

8. 59 + 44 + 68 = ______ 74 + 56 + 47 = ______ 38 + 87 + 27 = ______

9. 50 + 75 + 87 = ______ 29 + 71 + 53 = ______ 47 + 76 + 84 = ______

Strategies for Subtracting Whole Numbers

There are many ways to subtract whole numbers.
Here are some ways to subtract 1889 from 3497.

$$\begin{array}{r} 3497 \\ -\ 1889 \\ \hline \end{array}$$

1. If you add the same amount to both numbers, the difference will remain the same.

3497 + 3 = 3500
1889 + 3 = 1892

Now subtract 3500 – 1892.

3500 – 1800 = 1700
1700 – 92 = 1608

2. Round 1889 to 2000.

3497 – 2000 = 1497

Difference between rounded number and actual number:

2000 – 1889 = 111

1497 + 111 = 1608

3. Add in steps to get from 1889 to 3497.

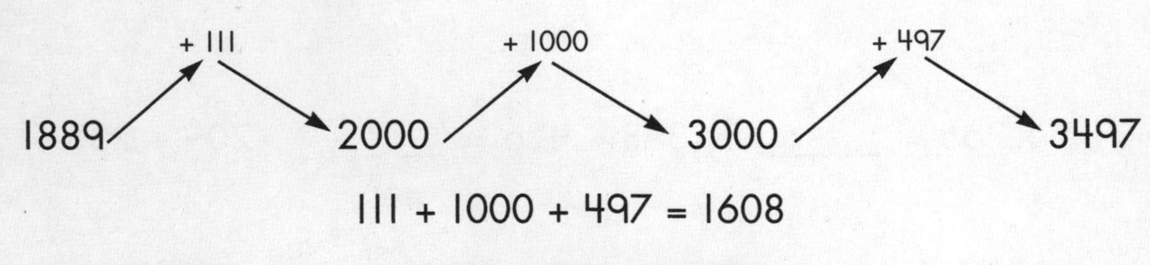

111 + 1000 + 497 = 1608

You added 1608 in all, so 3497 – 1889 = 1608.

4. More ones are needed. → Trade 1 ten for 10 ones. Subtract the ones. → Subtract the tens. → More hundreds are needed. Trade 1 thousand for 10 hundreds. Subtract the hundreds. → Subtract the thousands.

More ones are needed.	Trade 1 ten for 10 ones. Subtract the ones.	Subtract the tens.	More hundreds are needed. Trade 1 thousand for 10 hundreds. Subtract the hundreds.	Subtract the thousands.
3497 − 1889	(8, 17) 3497 − 1889 = 8	(8, 17) 3497 − 1889 = 08	(2, 14, 8, 17) 3497 − 1889 = 608	(2, 14, 8, 17) 3497 − 1889 = 1608

Subtraction: Whole Numbers (1)

1.	89 – 26	53 – 49	71 – 39	50 – 38
2.	507 – 268	391 – 149	600 – 252	768 – 29
3.	6841 – 586	3907 – 278	2000 – 899	3082 – 463
4.	7362 – 4809	9621 – 4376	8593 – 1869	7006 – 2534
5.	8209 – 2647	8004 – 7958	6732 – 4811	9494 – 2599
6.	7382 – 4593	1506 – 1062	3700 – 1290	8615 – 4923

Subtraction: Whole Numbers (2)

1.	16 284 – 8 031	29 408 – 5 729	62 000 – 9 899	37 509 – 6 222
2.	84 000 – 7 000	36 294 – 5 609	75 481 – 4 444	18 262 – 3 897
3.	24 319 – 8 648	53 628 – 7 305	76 151 – 9 258	20 400 – 6 380
4.	56 273 – 27 645	91 003 – 36 327	63 184 – 16 423	16 040 – 9 450
5.	63 214 – 17 628	81 191 – 54 327	73 624 – 18 587	80 043 – 20 327
6.	34 006 – 16 439	78 000 – 25 999	81 042 – 36 387	74 135 – 62 428

Subtraction: Whole Numbers (3)

1.	672 − 438	527 − 408	700 − 226	385 − 196	582 − 297
2.	862 − 409	304 − 216	753 − 486	973 − 280	510 − 286
3.	7682 − 4309	9625 − 376	8514 − 4807	6000 − 3854	7351 − 2468
4.	2204 − 1368	5086 − 4137	7622 − 4392	5786 − 3338	4896 − 1309
5.	7684 − 2493	2600 − 1826	9614 − 378	1407 − 862	5627 − 1386
6.	7777 − 4868	3579 − 1485	7070 − 2358	6624 − 3585	1700 − 1380
7.	2600 − 1484	1941 − 1837	4939 − 2586	7647 − 488	3781 − 1189

Subtraction: Whole Numbers (4)

Use mental math to find each difference.

1. 73 – 45 = ______	91 – 39 = ______	67 – 26 = ______
2. 84 – 57 = ______	71 – 18 = ______	74 – 38 = ______
3. 99 – 49 = ______	68 – 24 = ______	64 – 18 = ______
4. 52 – 27 = ______	49 – 33 = ______	86 – 45 = ______
5. 73 – 46 = ______	85 – 35 = ______	74 – 31 = ______
6. 740 – 96 = ______	502 – 75 = ______	825 – 29 = ______
7. 621 – 297 = ______	845 – 237 = ______	648 – 299 = ______
8. 423 – 199 = ______	425 – 97 = ______	637 – 490 = ______
9. 837 – 425 = ______	962 – 559 = ______	827 – 416 = ______

Strategies for Multiplying Whole Numbers

There are many ways to multiply whole numbers.
Here are some ways to multiply 768 by 12.

$$\begin{array}{r} 768 \\ \times\ 12 \\ \hline \end{array}$$

1.

Multiply the parts of 768 by 10.

$$\begin{aligned} 10 \times 700 &= 7000 \\ 10 \times 60 &= 600 \\ 10 \times 8 &= \underline{80} \\ & 7680 \end{aligned}$$

Multiply the parts of 768 by 2.

$$\begin{aligned} 2 \times 700 &= 1400 \\ 2 \times 60 &= 120 \\ 2 \times 8 &= \underline{16} \\ & 1536 \end{aligned}$$

$$7680 + 1536 = 8000 + 1100 + 110 + 6 = 9216$$

2.

Multiply the parts of 768 by 12.

$$\begin{aligned} 12 \times 700 &= 8400 \\ 12 \times 60 &= 720 \\ 12 \times 8 &= \underline{96} \\ & 9216 \end{aligned}$$

3.

Multiply 768 by 2.

$$\begin{array}{r} {\scriptstyle 1\,1} \\ 768 \\ \times\ 12 \\ \hline 1536 \end{array}$$

Multiply 768 by 10.

$$\begin{array}{r} {\scriptstyle 1\,1} \\ 768 \\ \times\ 12 \\ \hline 1536 \\ 7680 \\ \hline \end{array}$$

Add.

$$\begin{array}{r} 768 \\ \times\ 12 \\ \hline 1536 \\ 7680 \\ \hline 9216 \end{array}$$

Multiplication: Whole Numbers (1)

1. 82×4 | 96×7 | 75×5 | 64×6

2. 90×8 | 37×2 | 84×9 | 73×3

3. 77×8 | 54×6 | 49×5 | 70×7

4. 206×7 | 538×5 | 790×9 | 817×4

5. 632×6 | 518×8 | 694×3 | 372×6

6. 945×7 | 737×2 | 864×8 | 943×7

Multiplication: Whole Numbers (2)

1.

$$\begin{array}{r} 28 \\ \times\ 14 \\ \hline \end{array} \qquad \begin{array}{r} 64 \\ \times\ 26 \\ \hline \end{array} \qquad \begin{array}{r} 73 \\ \times\ 38 \\ \hline \end{array} \qquad \begin{array}{r} 87 \\ \times\ 96 \\ \hline \end{array}$$

2.

$$\begin{array}{r} 85 \\ \times\ 85 \\ \hline \end{array} \qquad \begin{array}{r} 63 \\ \times\ 18 \\ \hline \end{array} \qquad \begin{array}{r} 19 \\ \times\ 47 \\ \hline \end{array} \qquad \begin{array}{r} 95 \\ \times\ 54 \\ \hline \end{array}$$

3.

$$\begin{array}{r} 58 \\ \times\ 25 \\ \hline \end{array} \qquad \begin{array}{r} 70 \\ \times\ 48 \\ \hline \end{array} \qquad \begin{array}{r} 28 \\ \times\ 26 \\ \hline \end{array} \qquad \begin{array}{r} 42 \\ \times\ 33 \\ \hline \end{array}$$

4.

$$\begin{array}{r} 85 \\ \times\ 41 \\ \hline \end{array} \qquad \begin{array}{r} 57 \\ \times\ 27 \\ \hline \end{array} \qquad \begin{array}{r} 36 \\ \times\ 36 \\ \hline \end{array} \qquad \begin{array}{r} 73 \\ \times\ 72 \\ \hline \end{array}$$

5.

$$\begin{array}{r} 94 \\ \times\ 63 \\ \hline \end{array} \qquad \begin{array}{r} 89 \\ \times\ 72 \\ \hline \end{array} \qquad \begin{array}{r} 64 \\ \times\ 38 \\ \hline \end{array} \qquad \begin{array}{r} 27 \\ \times\ 40 \\ \hline \end{array}$$

Multiplication: Whole Numbers (3)

1.	$\begin{array}{r} 507 \\ \times\ 26 \\ \hline \end{array}$	$\begin{array}{r} 638 \\ \times\ 92 \\ \hline \end{array}$	$\begin{array}{r} 790 \\ \times\ 84 \\ \hline \end{array}$	$\begin{array}{r} 255 \\ \times\ 75 \\ \hline \end{array}$
2.	$\begin{array}{r} 482 \\ \times\ 93 \\ \hline \end{array}$	$\begin{array}{r} 369 \\ \times\ 35 \\ \hline \end{array}$	$\begin{array}{r} 975 \\ \times\ 62 \\ \hline \end{array}$	$\begin{array}{r} 376 \\ \times\ 43 \\ \hline \end{array}$
3.	$\begin{array}{r} 700 \\ \times\ 29 \\ \hline \end{array}$	$\begin{array}{r} 620 \\ \times\ 43 \\ \hline \end{array}$	$\begin{array}{r} 397 \\ \times\ 65 \\ \hline \end{array}$	$\begin{array}{r} 777 \\ \times\ 58 \\ \hline \end{array}$
4.	$\begin{array}{r} 409 \\ \times\ 33 \\ \hline \end{array}$	$\begin{array}{r} 536 \\ \times\ 94 \\ \hline \end{array}$	$\begin{array}{r} 482 \\ \times\ 73 \\ \hline \end{array}$	$\begin{array}{r} 626 \\ \times\ 61 \\ \hline \end{array}$
5.	$\begin{array}{r} 898 \\ \times\ 60 \\ \hline \end{array}$	$\begin{array}{r} 620 \\ \times\ 41 \\ \hline \end{array}$	$\begin{array}{r} 437 \\ \times\ 32 \\ \hline \end{array}$	$\begin{array}{r} 618 \\ \times\ 70 \\ \hline \end{array}$

Multiplication: Whole Numbers (4)

Use mental math to find each product.

1. $7 \times 80 =$ ______ $6 \times 52 =$ ______ $5 \times 15 =$ ______

2. $3 \times 49 =$ ______ $2 \times 75 =$ ______ $3 \times 99 =$ ______

3. $5 \times 25 =$ ______ $3 \times 24 =$ ______ $9 \times 12 =$ ______

4. $2 \times 128 =$ ______ $4 \times 221 =$ ______ $8 \times 125 =$ ______

5. $6 \times 210 =$ ______ $3 \times 150 =$ ______ $5 \times 120 =$ ______

6. $20 \times 35 =$ ______ $50 \times 44 =$ ______ $40 \times 13 =$ ______

7. $49 \times 30 =$ ______ $20 \times 30 =$ ______ $10 \times 37 =$ ______

8. $35 \times 40 =$ ______ $50 \times 60 =$ ______ $16 \times 25 =$ ______

9. $99 \times 10 =$ ______ $27 \times 40 =$ ______ $30 \times 15 =$ ______

Strategies for Dividing Whole Numbers

There are many ways to divide whole numbers.
Here are some ways to divide 4863 by 15.

$15\overline{)4863}$

1. Rename 4863 as a sum of numbers easily divided by 15.

4500 + 300 + 63
4500 ÷ 15 = 300
300 ÷ 15 = 20
63 ÷ 15 = 4 R. 3

320 + 4 = 324

4863 ÷ 15 = 324 R3

2. Multiply 15 by numbers you know will work, to get as close to 4863 as you can.

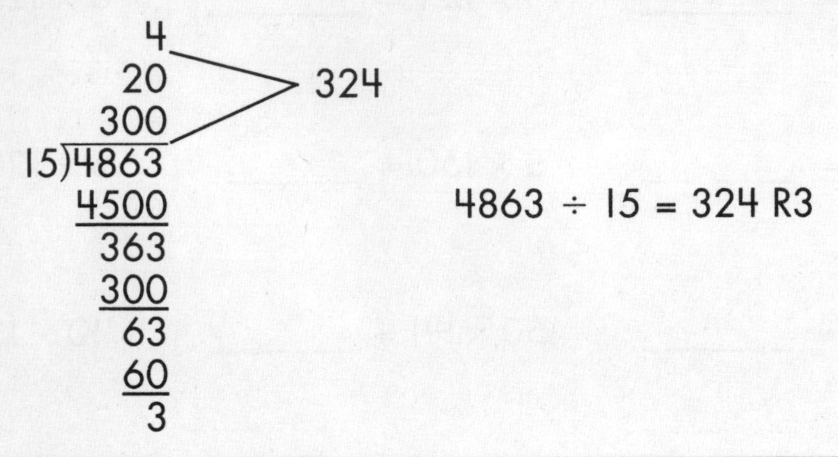

3.

Divide the hundreds. Multiply and subtract. →	Bring down the tens. →	Divide the tens. Multiply and subtract. →	Bring down the ones. →	Divide the ones. Multiply and subtract. →	Write the remainder.
Th H T O	Th H T O	Th H T O	Th H T O	Th H T O	Th H T O

```
     3          3            32            32           324         324 R3
15)4863    15)4863      15)4863       15)4863      15)4863      15)4863
   45         45↓          45            45           45           45
    3          36           36            36           36           36
                            30            30↓          30           30
                             6             63           63           63
                                                        60           60
                                                         3            3
```

Division: Whole Numbers (1)

1. $89 \div 9 =$ ________ $46 \div 4 =$ ________ $94 \div 7 =$ ________

2. $71 \div 4 =$ ________ $75 \div 5 =$ ________ $37 \div 8 =$ ________

3. $66 \div 6 =$ ________ $48 \div 4 =$ ________ $84 \div 2 =$ ________

4. $27 \div 6 =$ ________ $39 \div 5 =$ ________ $97 \div 8 =$ ________

5. $84 \div 3 =$ ________ $57 \div 7 =$ ________ $60 \div 4 =$ ________

6. $526 \div 4 =$ ________ $843 \div 6 =$ ________ $705 \div 5 =$ ________

7. $837 \div 3 =$ ________ $624 \div 4 =$ ________ $571 \div 2 =$ ________

8. $219 \div 8 =$ ________ $435 \div 7 =$ ________ $528 \div 9 =$ ________

9. $860 \div 9 =$ ________ $423 \div 6 =$ ________ $852 \div 8 =$ ________

10. $702 \div 4 =$ ________ $555 \div 4 =$ ________ $361 \div 6 =$ ________

Division: Whole Numbers (2)

1.	$8\overline{)59}$	$5\overline{)73}$	$9\overline{)68}$	$4\overline{)56}$
2.	$7\overline{)84}$	$2\overline{)37}$	$9\overline{)99}$	$8\overline{)85}$
3.	$6\overline{)732}$	$5\overline{)981}$	$7\overline{)844}$	$3\overline{)903}$
4.	$9\overline{)586}$	$4\overline{)734}$	$3\overline{)689}$	$5\overline{)275}$
5.	$2\overline{)840}$	$8\overline{)273}$	$8\overline{)864}$	$6\overline{)751}$
6.	$3\overline{)4687}$	$7\overline{)3535}$	$7\overline{)4685}$	$6\overline{)3404}$
7.	$4\overline{)3486}$	$2\overline{)5673}$	$5\overline{)8495}$	$9\overline{)7821}$

Division: Whole Numbers (3)

1. $26\overline{)75}$ $38\overline{)94}$ $18\overline{)93}$ $42\overline{)95}$

2. $47\overline{)368}$ $51\overline{)479}$ $32\overline{)584}$ $76\overline{)709}$

3. $30\overline{)278}$ $25\overline{)500}$ $34\overline{)374}$ $55\overline{)866}$

4. $25\overline{)4925}$ $62\overline{)3862}$ $28\overline{)7924}$ $37\overline{)3062}$

5. $24\overline{)2424}$ $40\overline{)8800}$ $52\overline{)5252}$ $95\overline{)6650}$

Division: Whole Numbers (4)

1. $15\overline{)87}$ $14\overline{)95}$ $12\overline{)84}$ $41\overline{)93}$ $24\overline{)86}$

2. $36\overline{)72}$ $28\overline{)86}$ $32\overline{)97}$ $63\overline{)98}$ $32\overline{)95}$

3. $46\overline{)385}$ $52\overline{)697}$ $85\overline{)408}$ $73\overline{)372}$ $82\overline{)689}$

4. $75\overline{)700}$ $37\overline{)480}$ $28\overline{)347}$ $63\overline{)896}$ $72\overline{)432}$

5. $37\overline{)4509}$ $24\overline{)3700}$ $86\overline{)6378}$ $91\overline{)4956}$ $88\overline{)7924}$

Division: Whole Numbers (5)

Use mental math to find each quotient.

1. $480 \div 6 =$ ______ $350 \div 7 =$ ______ $720 \div 9 =$ ______

2. $600 \div 5 =$ ______ $240 \div 2 =$ ______ $480 \div 8 =$ ______

3. $450 \div 9 =$ ______ $440 \div 4 =$ ______ $360 \div 6 =$ ______

4. $750 \div 25 =$ ______ $360 \div 18 =$ ______ $280 \div 14 =$ ______

5. $700 \div 35 =$ ______ $450 \div 15 =$ ______ $600 \div 12 =$ ______

6. $360 \div 90 =$ ______ $600 \div 20 =$ ______ $840 \div 42 =$ ______

7. $2000 \div 40 =$ ______ $4600 \div 23 =$ ______ $2700 \div 30 =$ ______

8. $7000 \div 35 =$ ______ $6300 \div 21 =$ ______ $9000 \div 45 =$ ______

9. $7500 \div 25 =$ ______ $7500 \div 15 =$ ______ $8400 \div 12 =$ ______

Strategies for Adding Decimal Numbers

There are many ways to add decimal numbers.
Here are some ways to add 3.725 and 4.970.

$$\begin{array}{r} 3.725 \\ +\ 4.970 \\ \hline \end{array}$$

1.

Add the whole numbers.	Add the tenths.	Add the hundredths.	Add the thousandths.
$\begin{array}{r} 3 \\ +\ 4 \\ \hline 7 \end{array}$	$\begin{array}{r} 0.700 \\ +\ 0.900 \\ \hline 1.600 \end{array}$	$\begin{array}{r} 0.020 \\ +\ 0.070 \\ \hline 0.090 \end{array}$	$\begin{array}{r} 0.005 \\ +\ 0.000 \\ \hline 0.005 \end{array}$

Combine the hundredths and thousandths: 0.090 + 0.005 = 0.095
Add in the tenths: 0.600 + 0.095 = 0.695
Add in the wholes: 7 + 1 + 0.695 = 8.695

2.

$$\begin{array}{r} 3.725 \\ +\ 4.970 \\ \hline 7.000 \\ 1.600 \\ 0.090 \\ 0.005 \\ \hline 8.695 \end{array}$$

3.

4.970 is 0.030 less than 5.

Add 5.
3.725 + 5 = 8.725

Subtract 0.030.
8.725 – 0.030 = 8.695

4.

Align the decimal points. →	Add the thousandths. →	Add the hundredths. →	Add the tenths. Trade 10 tenths for 1 one. →	Add the ones.
$\begin{array}{r} 3.725 \\ +\ 4.970 \\ \hline \end{array}$	$\begin{array}{r} 3.725 \\ +\ 4.970 \\ \hline 5 \end{array}$	$\begin{array}{r} 3.725 \\ +\ 4.970 \\ \hline 95 \end{array}$	$\begin{array}{r} 1 \\ 3.725 \\ +\ 4.970 \\ \hline 695 \end{array}$	$\begin{array}{r} 1 \\ 3.725 \\ +\ 4.970 \\ \hline 8.695 \end{array}$

Addition: Decimal Numbers (1)

1.

$$\begin{array}{r} 25.6 \\ +\ 14.3 \\ \hline \end{array} \qquad \begin{array}{r} 84.9 \\ +\ 27.6 \\ \hline \end{array} \qquad \begin{array}{r} 38.7 \\ +\ 8.6 \\ \hline \end{array} \qquad \begin{array}{r} 8.9 \\ +\ 7.3 \\ \hline \end{array}$$

2.

$$\begin{array}{r} 34.42 \\ +\ 6.38 \\ \hline \end{array} \qquad \begin{array}{r} 72.67 \\ +\ 49.53 \\ \hline \end{array} \qquad \begin{array}{r} 8.93 \\ +\ 7.48 \\ \hline \end{array} \qquad \begin{array}{r} 6.01 \\ +\ 9.99 \\ \hline \end{array}$$

3.

$$\begin{array}{r} 9.036 \\ +\ 3.495 \\ \hline \end{array} \qquad \begin{array}{r} 7.624 \\ +\ 8.735 \\ \hline \end{array} \qquad \begin{array}{r} 6.666 \\ +\ 6.666 \\ \hline \end{array} \qquad \begin{array}{r} 3.280 \\ +\ 5.967 \\ \hline \end{array}$$

4.

$$\begin{array}{r} 4.806 \\ +\ 9.376 \\ \hline \end{array} \qquad \begin{array}{r} 5.537 \\ +\ 9.685 \\ \hline \end{array} \qquad \begin{array}{r} 3.896 \\ +\ 7.409 \\ \hline \end{array} \qquad \begin{array}{r} 6.070 \\ +\ 4.039 \\ \hline \end{array}$$

5.

$$\begin{array}{r} 0.256 \\ +\ 0.597 \\ \hline \end{array} \qquad \begin{array}{r} 3.856 \\ +\ 0.484 \\ \hline \end{array} \qquad \begin{array}{r} 2.376 \\ +\ 9.406 \\ \hline \end{array} \qquad \begin{array}{r} 7.453 \\ +\ 8.491 \\ \hline \end{array}$$

6.

$$\begin{array}{r} 24.36 \\ +\ 24.537 \\ \hline \end{array} \qquad \begin{array}{r} 84.092 \\ +\ 9.43 \\ \hline \end{array} \qquad \begin{array}{r} 66.28 \\ +\ 0.249 \\ \hline \end{array} \qquad \begin{array}{r} 32.0 \\ +\ 49.362 \\ \hline \end{array}$$

Addition: Decimal Numbers (2)

1.	26.5 + 47.4 73.9	76.8 + 43.9 120.7	82.2 + 9.7 91.4	36.7 + 95.4	58.7 + 8.3
2.	26.24 + 18.40	37.07 + 48.28	67.24 + 8.93	75.41 + 84.59	36.25 + 47.32
3.	46.30 + 27.84	95.46 + 46.38	76.18 + 4.82	37.27 + 49.42	36.07 + 4.13
4.	4.564 + 9.385	7.629 + 4.856	9.357 + 2.643	4.004 + 0.528	6.352 + 9.448
5.	7.855 + 6.321	6.844 + 0.376	8.514 + 9.009	6.327 + 4.673	7.444 + 0.484
6.	9.625 4.324 + 8.107	6.313 7.004 + 6.455	3.771 4.856 + 7.403	7.665 0.459 + 2.350	6.256 8.149 + 3.040

Addition: Decimal Numbers (3)

Complete only those problems with sums greater than 100.

1.	34.6 + 65.7	29.5 + 42.3	76.3 + 42.8	17.4 + 80.3
2.	13.62 + 12.43	76.85 + 43.96	25.10 + 75.38	42.09 + 83.01
3.	28.63 + 14.75	84.32 + 19.16	17.09 + 90.43	25.75 + 74.26
4.	346.391 + 0.486	16.853 + 90.416	93.785 + 6.001	42.111 + 36.232
5.	48.201 2.513 + 13.204	0.262 9.305 + 13.446	75.251 13.486 + 14.002	33.333 27.142 + 40.253

Strategies for Subtracting Decimal Numbers

There are many ways to subtract decimal numbers.
Here are some ways to subtract 4.785 from 9.932.

$$\begin{array}{r} 9.932 \\ -\ 4.785 \\ \hline \end{array}$$

1.

If you add the same amount to both numbers, the difference will remain the same.

9.932 + 0.015 = 9.947
4.785 + 0.015 = 4.800

Now subtract 9.947 – 4.800.

9 – 4 = 5
0.947 – 0.800 = 0.147

→ 5.147

2.

First subtract the whole number parts.

9 – 4 = 5

Now subtract the decimal parts by adding up in steps from 0.785 to 0.932.

0.785 —(+ 0.015)→ 0.800 —(+ 0.132)→ 0.932

The difference is 0.015 + 0.132 = 0.147.

Now combine the wholes and the parts.

5 + 0.147 = 5.147

So 9.932 – 4.785 = 5.147.

3.

Align the decimal points. →	More thousandths are needed. Trade 1 hundredth for 10 thousandths. Subtract the thousandths. →	More hundredths are needed. Trade 1 tenth for 10 hundredths. Subtract the hundredths. →	Subtract the tenths. →	Subtract the ones.
$\begin{array}{r} 9.932 \\ -\ 4.785 \\ \hline \end{array}$	$\begin{array}{r} ^{2\,12} \\ 9.932 \\ -\ 4.785 \\ \hline 7 \end{array}$	$\begin{array}{r} ^{8\,12\,12} \\ 9.932 \\ -\ 4.785 \\ \hline 47 \end{array}$	$\begin{array}{r} ^{8\,12\,12} \\ 9.932 \\ -\ 4.785 \\ \hline .147 \end{array}$	$\begin{array}{r} ^{8\,12\,12} \\ 9.932 \\ -\ 4.785 \\ \hline 5.147 \end{array}$

Subtraction: Decimal Numbers (1)

1.

14.8	27.5	35.3	16.1
− 7.9	− 16.4	− 19.7	− 8.3

2.

27.32	43.01	36.41	17.33
− 14.56	− 12.20	− 8.04	− 16.42

3.

0.447	5.251	3.001	7.767
− 0.263	− 0.320	− 1.024	− 5.238

4.

9.462	7.357	6.636	2.568
− 4.341	− 2.004	− 4.804	− 0.381

5.

3.004	7.658	8.000	4.506
− 1.252	− 3.046	− 3.267	− 0.273

6.

76.27	31.0	76.3	6.3
− 8.104	− 19.310	− 14.209	− 6.014

Subtraction: Decimal Numbers (2)

1.	84.6 − 73.8	67.8 − 32.4	75.5 − 8.2	86.7 − 41.9	38.6 − 9.7
2.	27.5 − 14.8	30.8 − 22.4	26.2 − 14.0	95.7 − 48.6	30.2 − 24.9
3.	0.513 − 0.228	5.216 − 1.008	3.000 − 2.114	7.628 − 4.309	2.562 − 0.497
4.	7.662 − 4.857	9.314 − 4.945	7.362 − 4.180	2.001 − 1.004	6.350 − 4.045
5.	37.628 − 9.409	43.678 − 24.967	83.268 − 41.009	32.168 − 14.002	76.154 − 3.628
6.	41.234 − 0.138	76.259 − 43.183	39.006 − 8.458	51.408 − 42.567	73.121 − 8.005
7.	567.403 − 248.531	751.426 − 48.917	385.267 − 149.004	142.040 − 142.003	762.158 − 490.037

Subtraction: Decimal Numbers (3)

Complete only those problems with differences greater than 100.

1.

287.6	200.2	576.86	253.3
– 189.8	– 98.4	– 477.38	– 142.7

2.

368.24	3010.00	198.68	256.77
– 138.45	– 2909.87	– 98.01	– 49.38

3.

272.007	780.072	420.075	163.002
– 171.997	– 89.328	– 320.001	– 63.004

4.

527.082	672.420	300.250	199.999
– 409.093	– 500.936	– 203.516	– 99.436

5.

499.685	620.324	176.428	238.555
– 399.885	– 519.325	– 76.939	– 128.567

Strategies for Multiplying Decimal Numbers

There are many ways to multiply decimal numbers.
Here are some ways to multiply 4.367 by 8.

$$\begin{array}{r} 4.367 \\ \times \quad 8 \\ \hline \end{array}$$

1. Multiply by 8.

$8 \times 4 = 32$
$8 \times 0.300 = 2.400$
$8 \times 0.060 = 0.480$
$8 \times 0.007 = 0.056$

Add the wholes.

$32 + 2 = 34$

Add the parts.

$0.400 + 0.480 + 0.056 = 0.880 + 0.056$
$= 0.936$

Combine.

$34 + 0.936 = 34.936$

2. Multiply each part of 4.367 by 8, starting from the left.
Then add the parts.

$$\begin{array}{r} 4.367 \\ \times \quad 8 \\ \hline 32 \\ 2.400 \\ .480 \\ .056 \\ \hline 34.936 \end{array}$$

3. Multiply the thousandths. → Multiply and add the hundredths. → Multiply and add the tenths. → Multiply and add the ones. → Place the decimal point in the product.

$$\begin{array}{r} {}^{5} \\ 4.367 \\ \times \quad 8 \\ \hline 6 \end{array} \qquad \begin{array}{r} {}^{5\,5} \\ 4.367 \\ \times \quad 8 \\ \hline 36 \end{array} \qquad \begin{array}{r} {}^{2\,5\,5} \\ 4.367 \\ \times \quad 8 \\ \hline 936 \end{array} \qquad \begin{array}{r} {}^{2\,5\,5} \\ 4.367 \\ \times \quad 8 \\ \hline 34936 \end{array} \qquad \begin{array}{r} {}^{2\,5\,5} \\ 4.367 \\ \times \quad 8 \\ \hline 34.936 \end{array}$$

Multiplication: Decimal Numbers (1)

1.	2.8×3	5.7×9	6.9×4	1.4×9
2.	23.7×2	49.6×8	62.9×8	85.8×5
3.	5.27×3	6.39×7	8.72×2	7.89×6
4.	45.62×4	33.72×6	86.41×7	38.82×7
5.	76.51×2	90.32×5	41.04×9	82.73×5
6.	58.09×3	63.27×8	84.79×6	39.26×4

Multiplication: Decimal Numbers (2)

1.	$\begin{array}{r} 5.203 \\ \times \quad 7 \\ \hline \end{array}$	$\begin{array}{r} 8.626 \\ \times \quad 3 \\ \hline \end{array}$	$\begin{array}{r} 2.567 \\ \times \quad 9 \\ \hline \end{array}$	$\begin{array}{r} 1.589 \\ \times \quad 6 \\ \hline \end{array}$
2.	$\begin{array}{r} 0.417 \\ \times \quad 4 \\ \hline \end{array}$	$\begin{array}{r} 5.157 \\ \times \quad 8 \\ \hline \end{array}$	$\begin{array}{r} 7.542 \\ \times \quad 7 \\ \hline \end{array}$	$\begin{array}{r} 3.506 \\ \times \quad 5 \\ \hline \end{array}$
3.	$\begin{array}{r} 4.762 \\ \times \quad 5 \\ \hline \end{array}$	$\begin{array}{r} 24.006 \\ \times \quad 8 \\ \hline \end{array}$	$\begin{array}{r} 3.974 \\ \times \quad 7 \\ \hline \end{array}$	$\begin{array}{r} 6.003 \\ \times \quad 4 \\ \hline \end{array}$
4.	$\begin{array}{r} 7.396 \\ \times \quad 5 \\ \hline \end{array}$	$\begin{array}{r} 0.632 \\ \times \quad 6 \\ \hline \end{array}$	$\begin{array}{r} 6.158 \\ \times \quad 3 \\ \hline \end{array}$	$\begin{array}{r} 9.253 \\ \times \quad 5 \\ \hline \end{array}$
5.	$\begin{array}{r} 2.764 \\ \times \quad 7 \\ \hline \end{array}$	$\begin{array}{r} 8.532 \\ \times \quad 2 \\ \hline \end{array}$	$\begin{array}{r} 4.897 \\ \times \quad 8 \\ \hline \end{array}$	$\begin{array}{r} 1.038 \\ \times \quad 4 \\ \hline \end{array}$
6.	$\begin{array}{r} 7.268 \\ \times \quad 6 \\ \hline \end{array}$	$\begin{array}{r} 5.476 \\ \times \quad 2 \\ \hline \end{array}$	$\begin{array}{r} 8.531 \\ \times \quad 3 \\ \hline \end{array}$	$\begin{array}{r} 9.004 \\ \times \quad 9 \\ \hline \end{array}$

Multiplication: Decimal Numbers (3)

Complete only those problems with products greater than 50.

1.	10.2×8	6.9×6	5.2×7	8.9×6
2.	12.3×5	15.2×3	10.9×7	11.3×4
3.	5.23×9	6.94×8	9.03×4	8.75×2
4.	7.333×9	6.556×7	8.997×6	12.326×5
5.	6.954×8	7.004×3	7.013×9	25.001×2

Strategies for Dividing Decimal Numbers

There are many ways to divide decimal numbers.
Here are some ways to divide 0.432 by 8.

$8\overline{)0.432}$

1. Break 0.432 into parts that are easy to divide by 8.

$0.400 \div 8 = 0.05$
$0.032 \div 8 = 0.004$
→ 0.054

$0.432 \div 8 = 0.054$

2. $432 \div 8 = 54$

0.432 is 1 thousandth of 432, so the answer must be 1 thousandth of 54.

$54 \times 0.001 = 0.054$

So $0.432 \div 8 = 0.054$.

3.

Divide the ones. Record 0 ones. →	Divide the tenths. Record 0 tenths. →	Divide the hundredths. Multiply and subtract. →	Bring down the thousandths. →	Divide the thousandths. Multiply and subtract.
$8\overline{)0.432}$ quotient: 0.	$8\overline{)0.432}$ quotient: 0.0	$8\overline{)0.432}$ quotient: 0.05 40 3	$8\overline{)0.432}$ quotient: 0.05 40↓ 32	$8\overline{)0.432}$ quotient: 0.054 40 32 32 0

Division: Decimal Numbers (1)

1.	4)4.8	7)6.3	2)9.6	4)7.6
2.	6)5.4	5)0.4	3)4.8	7)8.4
3.	5)9.5	2)3.8	3)5.7	5)9.5
4.	6)15.6	8)18.4	6)16.8	2)42.8
5.	9)8.19	1)6.35	3)7.29	9)8.46
6.	8)7.44	7)8.05	4)7.44	6)8.52
7.	9)4.86	8)3.28	7)2.59	8)5.68

Division: Decimal Numbers (2)

1. 5)3.765 8)1.304 9)4.698 7)3.451

2. 4)0.556 6)7.398 5)4.005 3)9.999

3. 7)32.662 8)9.944 6)8.352 2)1.668

4. 7)14.007 2)9.034 5)4.960 8)6.320

5. 3)19.623 9)4.869 7)4.326 6)8.202

Division: Decimal Numbers (3)

Complete only those problems with quotients less than 1.

1. $9\overline{)8.64}$ $7\overline{)14.28}$ $2\overline{)1.38}$ $6\overline{)6.36}$

2. $8\overline{)27.36}$ $4\overline{)12.32}$ $2\overline{)0.44}$ $9\overline{)16.38}$

3. $5\overline{)5.005}$ $3\overline{)4.206}$ $4\overline{)12.64}$ $7\overline{)0.364}$

4. $4\overline{)2.372}$ $2\overline{)1.564}$ $9\overline{)27.657}$ $5\overline{)4.565}$

5. $8\overline{)0.736}$ $4\overline{)3.744}$ $6\overline{)0.006}$ $3\overline{)4.143}$

6. $9\overline{)4.005}$ $7\overline{)1.344}$ $5\overline{)1.345}$ $6\overline{)7.002}$